Tina Trapp's Guide to Craps

By Tina Trapp

As Told to Larry Edell

LEAF Press

San Diego, CA

Tina Trapp's Guide to Craps

By Tina Trapp

As Told to Larry Edell

Published by:
LEAF Press
P. O. Box 421440
San Diego, CA 92142-1440

First Printing 1996

ISBN: 0-9652215-0-4

Library of Congress Catalog Card Number: 96-76520

January

First, I'd like to thank you for buying this book. I really would have preferred to call it "The Hookers Guide to Craps," but the publisher didn't think it would sell. Even the "Exotic Dancers Guide to Craps" would have been better, but, if you'll pardon the pun, no dice. The fact is, I really did learn how to play craps as a "working girl." I'm strictly legit now, but to get the real story, you need to hear how it was. My name is really Tina Trapp and, due to some unusual circumstances that I describe later on, I've been getting a lot of publicity lately. Perhaps you've seen me on Letterman or Leno? It all had an indirect relationship to the game to craps. In fact, if I had never learned how to play craps, I would not be where I am today.

My first introduction to dice was, unfortunately, part of a scam. I was an exotic dancer then, well, actually a high class call girl, to be truthful. That particular night I was strolling through the flashing neon of the Fremont Street Experience. That's the pedestrian mall downtown. I love Las Vegas at night, the lights, the excitement and the adventure. I wasn't really looking for more business, but I should have known better. It was January, after all.

In January we have the world famous Consumer Electronics Show, along with its many adult oriented seminars and exhibitions. The X-Rated video industry is an integral part of the CES, and it attracts many men looking for an anything-goes-good-time, which can include a visit with a lady of the evening. But sex wasn't what this guy was looking for.

I had stopped in the Fremont, one of my favorite casinos and walked around, staring up at its wonderful old tin ceiling, and absorbing the energy from the people playing slot machines. As I passed by the table games, I noticed different areas of concentration, from the serious and studious blackjack players to the rowdy and noisy craps players. Craps seemed like a fun, energetic game, but I didn't have the slightest idea how to play. I walked back outside, and turned up on Third Street, toward the Lady Luck Parking Lot, where I had parked my car, when a Cadillac stopped in front of me. The door opened and a man about forty or so, not bad looking, stuck his head out the window and yelled "HEY HONEY, WANNA MAKE SOME MONEY?" Sure. Why not. Same-O Same-O. I got in his car and he said his name was Bill. He really looked good in his custom-made suit and muted silk tie. He was fit, clean shaven, and had blonde hair. Most of the guys that come here for conventions seem rumpled and red eyed after a day of pounding the pavement in the exhibit halls. Things were looking better and better. I snuggled up to him in the front seat.

"Look," Bill said, "I don't want sex, but I would like to take you into a casino and both of us can make a little cash. You interested?"

"Sure, I'll try anything once." I was very naive in those days and didn't worry too much about the niceties of the law or standard casino practices.

"OK. How much do you know about the game of craps?" When I told him that I knew absolutely nothing, I thought that I'd be heading home alone but actually he was very pleased.

"Great," he said. "Then you won't have to pretend. Things will go much better. Here's what we do. I'll go to the craps table first. You can walk around or have a drink, but wait a few minutes before you come looking for me. Then go to the same table but stand at the other end. Just talk to the people, ask them questions, be friendly. Go with the flow, OK?"

"Sounds good to me." I really didn't know a thing about the game then. Sure I'd seen it played lots of times, very confusing, people yelling and throwing chips all over. And I assumed you had to know a lot about math and odds and stuff like that. Well, this would certainly be a learning experience - for sure.

We drove back into the valet parking at the Golden Nugget, probably the fanciest downtown hotel. It is *very* classy. They always treat everyone right at the Nugget. It looks like an early 1900's San Francisco cabaret, with its crystal chandeliers and slowly revolving ceiling fans. They also have some genuine gold nuggets on display. When we went inside Bill showed me where the craps tables were, and I went to have a drink at a nearby bar. A few minutes later I found Bill at the table, and walked to the opposite side. He had given me $50 to "buy in", which I did and got ten five-dollar chips. His only other instruction was to "bet on the pass line, honey, the best bet in the house."

People stared at me while I was standing there. I had on a red halter top with red shorts. I'm about 5'3" (actually, I'm 5'2 ½") with 38DD hooters, that really filled out my top. My long, brown, permed hair fell just below my shoulders and I had a habit of tossing it out of the way. I guess Bill picked me out because I was a real attention-getter. And I did get attention - everyone was staring at my boobs. Normally I wouldn't go into my physical attributes in such detail, but I want you to get the full picture and understand just how my craps education really started.

I stood next to a cute brunette and we started talking. Her name was Barbara and she was there with her husband from

Poughkeepsie, New York. He had just finished playing blackjack and was watching her play craps. Then he started watching me, but Barbara didn't seem to mind. She said she bets on the "Field" because there are so many numbers. I told her I had never played before, and looked around for the "pass line". I could see where it said "field" and "pass" on the table but I still didn't know what to do.

I thought I was really disappointing Bill, who wasn't looking at me at all. Suddenly, someone with a big stick pushed the dice toward me.

"Wanna shoot lady?" he said.

My two new craps table-mates nodded their heads yes.

"Sure . . . only . . . I've never done this before . . . can someone tell me what to do?"

Everyone started helping at once. They were really friendly! Maybe it was my cleavage, I don't know. So, finally, according to everyone's instructions, I picked up two of the dice and pushed one of chips on the "pass" area. I threw Mr. Dice slowly toward the other end of the table where Bill was standing.

"Seven, winner seven, the virgin threw a winner," the man with the stick said. Everyone clapped and cheered! I couldn't believe it. This was great! I had won $5!

Then Bill said, "A virgin craps player. I think she'll throw for a long time, dealer. $10 on the pass line for the virgin." He put some chips down, at his end of the table.

I left the two chips on the pass line and picked up the dice and threw them again. Uh oh, an eleven came up this time, but everyone cheered wildly! I didn't throw another seven and had no idea what all the cheering was about! And then suddenly *everyone* started betting in a strange language I didn't understand.

"Five dollar yo for the shooter."

"Ten dollar pass for the shooter."

"Shooter, shooter, shooter."

"Four dollar horn, one for the dealer." Incomprehensible.

By some absolute miracle I threw another seven. People crowded into the table. Hundreds of dollars were plunked on the pass line. I looked down at the space in front of me and it looked like there were five or ten chips there. I picked up the dice and threw them again, very slowly, and, bummer, an eight came up. People still cheered, even though no one won anything and I didn't roll a seven. How does this strange game work, I wondered. It sure was fun though!

Bill said, "I think this little lady will be here for a long time, Dealer. Hard six and eight for the shooter." Then, to my great surprise, other people started making more strange bets for "the virgin shooter". That was me, I guess.

"All the hard ways for the shooter,"

"Four dollar horn for the shooter,"

"Hard eight for the shooter."

Even Barbara's husband bet $5 on the field for the shooter. I scooped up my chips and put two of them ($10) down on the pass line. This was fun, even if I didn't know what I was doing. I picked up the dice and threw them again, very slowly . . . a four. More cheers. But I couldn't imagine why. I didn't roll an eight or a seven or an eleven. This was *very* confusing.

"Hard four for the shooter," someone said.

"Press my hard eight for the shooter," and so on. Chips were flying everywhere.

"The point is eight," said the man with a stick.

Well, I rolled and rolled. It seemed like every number kept coming up over and over again, except the eight. But people kept betting for me and cheering wildly. I couldn't understand why were they doing that when I didn't throw an eight. The dealers were paying everyone and I had *lots* of chips in front of me and lots more in my "rack", that area of the table where you can rest your arms or whatever else happens to land there. Pretty soon I started cheering too, forgetting whether I should roll an eight, a four, or a seven. How did this game work? Everyone just kept yelling, betting and throwing chips all over the table! Finally, after what seemed forever, I rolled an eight, only it was hard (???) and everyone went berserk, yelling and screaming at the top of their lungs! People from the other tables came over to see what was going on. I had a pile of chips in front of me and I started to pick them up and noticed they were all different colors.

I was ready to leave, more confused than anything else, when the stick person pushed Mr. Dice at me again, and said, "same shooter." Oh, no. Did he really mean me? I looked at Bill pleadingly, and he shook his head yes. Gingerly, I picked up the dice, and threw them slowly, and a seven came up. It was going to be a long, but exciting night.

Finally, after what seemed like hours, I threw another seven, but no one cheered this time. After a few silent seconds, they all started applauding, yelling "great shooting", and similar things of endearment to a virgin. I didn't exactly know why the second seven didn't win, but someone else got to play for a while. I looked up at Bill and he was gone. This was my signal to leave too, so I scooped up my chips and left amid the applause.

I met Bill back at the valet park, as agreed. I had thousands of questions, but all I got out of him was "not now, wait til we get in the car." So we got in the car and he said "not now wait til we get to the hotel."

We drove in silence out of downtown and up the strip to the Desert Inn. I tried asking my questions but all I got was a secret little smile, a sidelong glance and a promise to explain all when we got to the hotel. The silent treatment continued as the valet took the car and I followed Bill up to his room. Sex never entered my mind. I wanted to know about craps. We took our chips out and counted them. I had $1,815. He had $670. Quite a haul for two hours work.

"Okay," he said. "Let me explain some things. Craps virgins, like you were, *always* have good luck. I was afraid to explain more about the game, because then you wouldn't be a virgin anymore. That's why I was so glad to hear that you knew nothing about it. Whenever virgins play they win, and I helped things along by getting people to place bets for you. You can keep all the money you won, by the way. It's yours."

"But what went on? Why didn't I win on that seven? What's a hard way? What's a Yo? What's . . . ?"

"Hold on," Bill said. "You're really interested, aren't you?"

"Oh yes! It was so exciting, everyone cheering and yelling. "Please teach me how to play!"

So he taught me - the basics anyway. Bill told me that since each die has six numbers, a total of 36 different combinations can be made. He took out a pad of paper which had D.I. on it, for the Desert Inn, and added a C.E. to it so it said DICE. Corny but cute!

If all of the 36 different combinations are written out, it would look like the table on the next page.

Number	Combinations	Ways to make
2	1+1	1
3	2+1, 1+2	2
4	3+1, 1+3, 2+2	3
5	4+1, 1+4, 3+2, 2+3	4
6	5+1, 1+5, 4+2, 2+4, 3+3	5
7	6+1, 1+6, 5+2, 2+5, 4+3, 3+4	6
8	6+2, 2+6, 3+5, 5+3, 4+4	5
9	6+3, 3+6, 5+4, 4+5	4
10	6+4, 4+6, 5+5	3
11	6+5, 5+6	2
12	6+6	1

He said that the game of craps revolves around the number seven, because that number can be made in more ways than any other number. The "odds" of another number rolling are always calculated with respect to the seven.

For example, to calculate the odds of a four rolling I could see that a four had three combinations and the seven had six combinations. So the odds are six to three (or 2:1) that a seven will roll before a four. This means also that for every four rolled, a seven should roll twice and there is twice the chance that a seven will roll before a four.

The ten will roll the same as the four, 2:1.

But, look at the six and eight. Each has five ways of rolling, compared to six ways for the seven. So the odds are 6:5 for both the six and the eight.

This means, in practical terms, if I bet five dollars on the six or eight and it rolls before the seven, I should win $6. If, however, I bet $5 on the four or ten I should win $10.

The numbers look like this:

Numbers	Odds related to seven	
4 & 10	6:3	(or 2:1)
6 & 8	6:5	
11 & 3	6:2	(or 3:1)
2 & 12	6:1	
5 & 9	6:4	(or 3:2)

This looks pretty good for the two and twelve. If I bet $5 on either number, I should get $30 back. However, Bill reminded me that the odds of the two or twelve rolling before the seven are only one in six. That's how the odds are calculated in the first place. A seven should roll six times to each one roll of the two or twelve. So, the numbers with the best odds are the six and eight.

At least those are the numbers that roll the most often next to the seven.

My brain had just about had it. After all, it was 2:30 in the morning. I had kind of assumed that I would sleep with Bill but he said he was beat, maybe tomorrow. He must have seen how tired I was because he took pity on me and didn't send me home. But, there was only one bed.

"Well, we'll sleep together, but that's about it." He took off his clothes, all but his shorts, and climbed into bed. I removed all of my clothes, turned off the lights, and crawled in, snuggling in against him. Reaching over, I found one of those hard ways I had been hearing so much about all night. Pretty soon he had turned around and was touching my breasts, kissing them, kissing me, and then he was in me. It felt so good to have him there, drawing out my pleasure in this wonderful city of lights, excitement, and craps! He came very quickly and was soon asleep.

I guess I'm not a virgin anymore.

February

Las Vegas is cold in February, but cold or not, the Conventions keep on coming. This month it's home builders and construction workers. There is some kind of convention here almost every week, all year long. Men like to come here, far from home, and have their companies pay for their fun - fun unlike anything they can get at home!

My second craps experience was with Harry, a guy who I met through the out call service I belong to. He was, as usual, married, wealthy and far from home. I got the feeling that he didn't want to sleep with me just for sex. He wanted to put something over on his wife, Bonnie. He talked about her all the time.

"You're so much thinner than Bonnie," and

"You've got much better breasts than Bonnie," and

"You're so much prettier than Bonnie," and so forth.

It got me thinking why so many men *need* prostitutes. Maybe it isn't their sex drive. Maybe it's their sneaky drive. They think that they can get away with something secret, and forbidden, without their wives' knowledge.

Anyway, Harry was in his fifties, slightly paunchy, slightly balding, and slightly intelligent. He told me all about Bonnie and their two children. They all lived in a suburb of Chicago where he was an executive in a company that built department stores. Bonnie was "just a housewife, never wanted anything else," he said. Sometimes I wish I could talk to the wives, to get their side of the story. I guess if men actually told their wives about their little flings, and they accepted it, that would take all the excitement and secrecy away. Oh, well, business is business.

It was late, and Harry wanted me to spend the night (hey, anything for a client and he *was* paying extra). He was a boring, unimaginative lover and complained about Bonnie the whole time. Sheesh, the things I used to do for money.

The next morning though, he was very nice, and took me to a great Italian restaurant off the strip, for brunch. In the course of the conversation he asked if I liked to gamble and I said I was "learning" craps. He got real quiet for a second and then whispered that he knew a "secret" way of winning and would show it to me since I was so good to him. I suppose that translated into "so much better than Bonnie". We finished eating and drove to the Mirage, which was his favorite casino.

The Mirage is one of my favorites too. It's classy and gaudy at the same time. There is a huge realistic looking volcano outside that erupts in flashes of lava and lights every half hour at night! They have rare white tigers, a dolphin pool, nice people, and terrific rooms. I had been there before. And their Siegfried and Roy Variety and Magic Show is probably the best show in the world, even though it's also the most expensive in Las Vegas.

Entering the casino, we walked through a 90' atrium, complete with palm trees and waterfalls! You really feel like you're in the middle of a tropical rainforest! We also saw the huge salt water aquarium and the two nude mermaid statues. There was marble and teak everywhere.

We walked back to the craps tables and bought in. Harry gave me $100 and he bought in for $500. I had planned to play with my own money but, hey, he could afford it.

First, he started to explain to me what a "hard way" was. If a number rolled that had two identical dice, this was "hard". For example, a six could be rolled 4 & 2, 5 & 1, or 3 & 3. The

3 & 3 roll is a "hard six". A 4 & 4 is a "hard eight", a 2 & 2 is a "hard four", and a 5 & 5 is a "hard ten".

He also explained that the first roll a "shooter" makes is the "come out" roll. If a seven or eleven is rolled, everyone on the pass line wins. If a two, three or twelve is rolled, everyone on the pass line loses. If a 4, 5, 6, 8, 9 or 10 is rolled, that number becomes the "point". Then, if that point repeats before a seven is rolled, the pass line bettors win. If a seven rolls, however, the pass line bettors lose.

So, a seven is a winner *before* the point is established, and a loser *after* the point is established.

Harry didn't bet anything for a while, until a point was rolled that had a possible "hard way" (a 4, 6, 8 or 10). Harry's secret turned out to be betting $20 on the hard way whenever a point with a possible hard way was established. Since the hard six or eight paid nine-to-one, and the hard four or ten paid seven-to-one, Harry could win a bunch of money. Unfortunately he ended up losing most of the time, but said that if he lost five times and won only once, he would still be way ahead. For example, if he bet $20 on five consecutive hard ways and lost, he would be behind $100. But if he won just the sixth hard way, he would win $140 for the ten or four, and $180 for the six or eight!

We played for an hour or so. I was betting on the pass line only, and ended up $50 ahead. I'm not sure what Harry did. I was too engrossed in my own bets and figuring out the game, but he said he won over $100. "Terrific," I said, enthusiastically! I gave him his $100 back and waited for him to tell me to keep it. I kept waiting. What a jerk!

Just before we stopped playing, the strangest thing happened. An old man with dark glasses was led to the table by a younger, nurse type woman. It looked like he was blind and everybody kept wondering what they would do. They didn't do anything at all, until his turn to roll came up.

He said he wanted to shoot and had his helper put $10 down on the pass line. When the stick man pushed the dice over to him, he reached down and caressed the red cubes, like he was talking to them through his fingers. Then picked out two, paused for a second, held them up in the air and said "six". He rolled a six! Harry immediately put $20 on the hard six and I put $10 on the pass line.

Then the old man held them up to the sky again and said to his companion, "Put $120 on the eight." And, of course, he rolled an eight, then he took his bet and winnings down. He lifted the dice again and you could have heard a pin drop, but he didn't say a thing. He made no bet and he sevened out!

No one said a word, not even Harry, as the blind man picked up his $130 in winnings and slowly walked away. Perhaps he *saw* a seven coming and didn't want to voice it out loud, which Harry later said was very bad luck. Finally, after a few seconds of total silence, play resumed, and the players started talking again.

"Wow, that guy sure could call 'em," and

"Blind people have special powers," and

"Shoulda put a thousand on the eight," and so on.

It got me to wondering if the shooter really could influence the dice by using his mind. Or if someone could predict what the outcome of a roll would be. There are lots of so-called psychics out there who claim special powers. Maybe some of them can predict the dice, like some others tell fortunes. Who knows? But I knew then that if I were ever to see someone who seemed certain of what he was doing, I would back him up with a big bet.

Harry, of course, didn't believe in any of this, probably because he lost money on the blind guy. He had to go to some meeting, so he asked if he could drop me off somewhere. I said no thanks, I'd stay there.

He left and I just watched for a while. I was determined to learn this game. Pretty soon, though, I got tired of the Yo's, Horns, and other things I didn't understand so I left the table and walked around. The Mirage really is a magical place. They have a wonderful Dolphin Pool, and I often went there to talk to the dolphins. I wandered over there and sat down at the edge of the pool. *Hey, can you guys understand me?* I beamed at them. No response. I wondered if the blind guy could talk to them.

I started reminiscing about being a little girl in junior high, back in good ole Brooklyn. I was taking a test and didn't know the answer to a question so I concentrated on reading the teacher's mind. I did get an answer to the question from somewhere, and it turned out to be correct. Maybe I had known it deep inside all the time. Who knows?

I went back to the craps table and just stood there, trying to predict which number would roll. I got two numbers right and twelve wrong. So much for psychic powers.

I stood there for a while longer, watching, and noticed that someone else was playing the hard ways, the way Harry did. She was young, blonde, kinda cute. I watched her play for a while, but she didn't bet very often and it was difficult to see what she was doing. Finally I figured it out.

She waited until a ten or four rolled. Then, she would bet $40 against the ten or four and, at the same time, she would bet $5 on the hard way of the same number. It looked like she was betting against herself. Soon, however, she had amassed a bunch of chips and left the table.

I followed her and asked about her playing. I've found that craps players are very friendly and I certainly didn't look threatening to her. We went over to a lounge with a piano player and I treated us both to banana daiquiris.

The blonde was Doris from Los Angeles, in Las Vegas with her husband, who was at a meeting. They were both in their thirties and in the computer field. She loved the game of craps and was happy to tell me about her system.

She explained that a ten and four can each only be rolled two basic ways. A ten can be a 6 + 4 or 5 + 5 and four can be rolled as 3 + 1 or 2 + 2. She always bet $40 against the four or ten and bet the hard way at the same time. If a hard ten or four rolled, for example, she would lose the $40 but win $45 on the hard way. It was an "insurance" bet. She always waited for the four or ten to roll once, so the chances of it rolling again before the seven were very small. When the seven rolled, she would win $20 on the "no-four" and lose $5 on the hard way, giving her a $15 profit. She would only lose then, when the "soft" four rolled which, according to her, hardly ever happened.

This seemed like a terrific system to me at the time, but later I found several faults. One of them is that occasionally the soft ten or four would roll twice before the seven and she would be out $45. So she would need more than two wins just to get even. Further, when she bets against the number, the odds are reversed, so instead of paying $80 on a $40 bet, she would only win $20. Finally, the ten or four could be rolled three ways, not two — two soft ways and one hard way. I didn't know most of this at the time so I couldn't point it out to her. I also didn't know at the time that you had to actually pay a commission of 5% to the casino for the privilege on betting against the number!

We chatted for a while and then we both left. She seemed to have a pretty good system, but it was boring and she really didn't make much money. And, worst of all, when a seven rolled, everyone else at the table lost while she won. Later, I found out she was called a "wrong" bettor, since she was betting that the seven would roll before the point. Someone who bets on the point rolling before the seven is called a "right" bettor. Also, she could never get excited and scream and yell when she won because everyone else would probably kill her. If she won, they all lost!

She might make a little money here and there but it's not exciting as it is playing on the pass line. Besides I like getting $40 when I bet $40. Getting $20 for a $40 bet seems counterproductive.

Deep in thought, I walked outside, back toward the dolphins. I sat next to the pool and thought about Doris, the blind man, and craps. When I looked up, a dolphin was staring right into my eyes. How did I do that, I thought. I reached out to pet him and he was gone.

March

March is a month of transition for Las Vegas. The swimming pools are refurbished and preparations are being made for the summer months. March also has conventions for the construction and clothing industries. And personally, March was the month for my worst craps experience, ever.

I had a very limited knowledge of craps at the time, but I thought I knew a lot. It struck me that I could make my living at craps if I came up with a good system.

I had saved some money up in the past few years, because I was getting really tired of hooking, and sex just wasn't fun anymore. I wanted a normal life, and I thought that a few big craps wins would give it to me.

Walking around in the casinos, I saw couples kissing, families having fun, people participating in the normal workings of the world. I was lonely, with only a few close friends and no family. Both my mother and father had died years ago. They were heavy smokers and both died of cancer within a couple of years of each other.

I had a fairly normal childhood. My family wasn't dysfunctional like the families of some of the kids I grew up with. I'm an only child, born twenty-nine years ago in New York City. It's hard to believe that next year is the big 3-0. My parents sent me to college, Boston University, and I did well for the first year as an accounting major. Then my Mom died and I came home and got a job as an accountant in Queens. It didn't pay much since I didn't have my degree, but at least I was with my Dad and we kept each other company.

Two years later he died and I decided to change my life. I was left with a house which I promptly sold and moved to the Golden State, California. I was going to be a Star.

In Hollywood I found various jobs as a lounge singer, accountant, waitress and, finally, prostitute. My small 5'3" build and my large bust made my body more attractive to the men I met than my mind. I found that I could make much more money selling my body than my accounting skills. Besides, I was just doing this until my big break came. Then, one of the bars I was working in closed down and the owner wanted to move to Las Vegas and take me with him. He was married, of course, and although the subject wasn't brought up, I knew I would continue to have sex with him, in order to keep my job as a topless dancer.

He and his wife moved to Las Vegas and I followed a week later, paying for my own apartment. He opened a nightclub and I danced and waited tables but things just didn't work out. He was involved in some illegal doings and somehow lost his liquor license. We started fighting and I started working in other clubs, first as a waitress, then as a topless dancer, and finally I went to an out-call service.

I weighed my choices and decided this was the best for the time being. The money from my parent's house was almost gone and I finally acknowledged that my voice would never get me to the big time and I definitely didn't have the desire to go back to college. Unlike a lot of the working girls back in Hollywood, I actually enjoyed hooking, for the most part. Maybe I was just lucky, but I had never gotten beaten up and I was usually able to call the shots about what I would and wouldn't do. Also, I never, ever did drugs. I figured I might as well use my homegrown assets to take control of my life and support myself.

Working the streets of Las Vegas served me well. I

managed to make over $50,000 a year, and saved up over $40,000 in just six years. Although I didn't have any moral problems with hooking, I always envied those families I saw doing things together. I kept thinking I would go back to school, get married and settle down, but I just never did it.

Now, I thought that if I played craps professionally I could earn at least another $20,000 easily and settle down somewhere. I would get a respectable job, meet my Prince Charming, have a family and get a house with a picket fence and a dog.

I came up with an unbeatable craps system, or so I thought. It was based on Doris' no-ten and no-four bets. I would wait until a four or ten rolled twice, bet against it, and bet the hard way. If I lost on a soft number, I would just double my bet the next time. The chance of a soft four or ten rolling was only eighteen to one. The chance of two soft fours or tens rolling was a whopping thirty-six to one. And, three soft tens or fours rolling before the seven was an insurmountable fifty-four to one!

So, my unbeatable plan was to keep betting and doubling my bets each time if I lost. I would win thousands, certainly. Keep in mind, I didn't really know how to play. Just the basics. Shoulda known better.

The casino I picked was Treasure Island, right next to the Mirage. They have a terrific real-life pirate battle outside every few hours, with moving (and sinking!) ships, cannons, and explosions! And the entire casino and hotel are done with a *very* classy pirate motif. I've always liked pirates.

I had taken $2,000 out of my savings earlier that afternoon, fantasizing about how I would be back the next day with a deposit of $10,000! After an early evening session with a totally forgettable client, I drove straight over to the T.I. I walked around the craps area a bit - it's right on the main aisle where people walk from the parking lot out to the front of the casino to see the pirate show. I finally found a table I liked, one that seemed to have the right karma. I wasn't nervous at all. After all, how could I lose? I had thought of a brand new system which just had to win. I was so lucky that no one had thought of it before.

I stood at the table for a few minutes and sure enough, two fours in a row rolled! I "laid" $40 against the four and put $5 on the hard four. Then as luck would have it, two tens rolled! $40 on the no-ten and $5 on the hard ten. A few rolls later, the shooter sevened out. I had won $20 on the ten and $20 the four, but lost $10 on the hard ways, net gain of $30. I had made $30 in ten minutes. I was on my way!

Soon I won another $30 the same way! $60 in less than half an hour! I was a genius! Some time later, two fours rolled again. $40 on the no-four, $5 on the hard four. Then, of all things, a soft four. So I doubled my no-four to $80 and my hard way to $10. Then, unbelievably, two tens rolled. Now I had $40 on the no-ten, $5 on the hard ten, $80 on the no-four, and $10 on the hard four. Of course, a soft ten rolled.

Now, the chances of four soft fours or tens rolling were seventy-two to one. But, somehow they both rolled and I doubled my bets again. To make matters worse, yet another soft ten rolled. Now I had $320 on both the no-ten and the no-four, and $40 each on the hard ten and four. I realized I was in deep trouble as Treasure Island had a $500 bet limit. Needless to say I lost both numbers again and I had to stop. Lucky thing, because the shooter kept on rolling numbers including another soft four and a hard ten (too late).

I had lost $40 + $80 + $160 + $320 plus the hard ways of $5 + $10 + $20 + $40 on both numbers - a total of $1,350 plus the vigs which I'll explain later. When I realized what I had done I was paralyzed. I couldn't move. I just stood there, numb.

One of the guys from the pit came up to me and told me how much they valued my business, blah, blah, blah. I still don't remember everything. Shock does that to people. Anyway he ended up giving me vouchers for a free night's stay and two meals. Big deal. I stuffed them in my pocket and drove home.

Sleep was out of the question so after I had calmed down a bit, I took a hard look at just what had happened. I found I had made some terrible mistakes. The worst of those mistakes was that I forgot the four and ten only pay 1:2 on don't bets. If I bet $80 I would only win $40. So if I lost $40 and $80, for a total of $120, and I doubled the $80 bet to $160 and won, I would only win back $80 so it wouldn't be enough to cover my losses. Almost every bet I was making, even if I was winning, was losing me money. I was doomed to defeat.

When I was a teenager, my dad always told me, "Tina, look at life as a learning experience." I guess I learned that I needed to get to know craps a lot better before I would try something like that again. And, I learned that I would not *discover* something that no one had ever thought of before.

Dawn was just breaking when I finally fell asleep, absolutely exhausted. It was early afternoon when I awakened. I felt refreshed and, surprisingly, not at all depressed. My subconscious must have been working all night, thinking of how to take my Dad's advice and *really* learn something useful. A cup of coffee cleared the last of the cobwebs and I studied my figures from the night before. It occurred to me that if I went somewhere with no table limits, and I tripled my losing bets instead of doubling them, my system might work. But what if eight or nine soft fours or tens rolled? Everything is possible in a game of chance. There had to be some way of winning this game. I was determined to make something of myself and, at the time, I thought that craps could do it.

I found the Treasure Island vouchers and wondered exactly what they were. I called T.I. and spoke to a very nice woman, who said she was a casino host. She told me that T.I. and every other casino had a "comp" system for its gamblers. She said that if I made bets of at least $25, my gambling would be tracked and I would become a rated player. I could get a comp club card which I would give to the pit boss whenever I started gambling. Depending on how long I gambled and the size of my bets, I would get "credits" which I could use for rooms (unnecessary), food (very necessary) or merchandise (??). This was pretty interesting but the importance of these comp club cards didn't hit me until a few days later.

The blinking red light of my answering machine beckoned so I checked my messages. The out call service had two clients for me, one tomorrow and one the next day. I had nothing for today so I decided to go back to T.I., get my comp card and a free dinner. I called back and talked to the same casino host again. I told her that I would be coming back for dinner and she suggested that I go to the pit and pick up my comp card.

As luck would have it, the same guy who gave me the vouchers was there. He gave me my card on the spot and said he had been holding it for me. It was a black card with holes punched in it.

I didn't feel like playing right then, but I was hungry, so I wandered over to the buffet area. Before I could even see the buffet entrance, I ran into a line a mile long, snaking around the edges of the casino. No way was I going to wait an hour just to get a free meal. Then, I saw someone walk to the front of the line and get in before everyone else did. Hmm. I went up there and waited. Sure enough, someone else came, showed his black card, and they let him in. Wow! I had discovered something for sure. I walked to the front of the line, showed my black card and voucher and they let me in too!

The meal was great and the voucher also let me have two free drinks, banana daiquiris, of course. And, the best part was that I didn't have to wait in line. I decided right then and there to investigate this comp card business a lot further.

On the way out I happened to glance at a newspaper display. On the front page of the Las Vegas Review-Journal, the headline read:

BINIONS LOSES $500K
IN CRAPS BET AGAIN

Well, that got my attention so I fished around in my purse for the right change and bought it. The article said that for the second time in six months, Binions Horseshoe in downtown Las Vegas, had lost a large craps bet. The Horseshoe, it seems, is world famous for taking any craps bet, but they had lost the last two out of three big ones. The smallest of those had been $250K. I figured that they more than made up for it with all publicity they got, win or lose. I had never been to Binions, and the night was still young, so I drove downtown and parked in their garage.

After six years of living in Las Vegas, and working in my particular profession, you might think that I would have seen all the casinos enough times to have the layouts memorized. In fact, until my recent craps experiences, I usually only passed through the casinos enough to get to the hotel section. All of the hotels force you to walk through the casinos to get to the rooms. Occasionally, I would meet someone at the bar for drinks first, or kill a couple of minutes playing quarter slots, but that was about it. And, I hardly ever had a client downtown since the strip saw most of the action. So it wasn't really that unusual that I hadn't been to Binions's before.

The Horseshoe was a large, rambling, dimly lit place. I stumbled across a display of $10,000 bills with the sign, HAVE YOUR PICTURE TAKEN IN FRONT OF A MILLION DOLLARS. Pretty nifty.

There were *lots* of craps tables. I found an empty one with the crew hovering around. Maybe I could get some questions answered. There were three men and one woman there. I found out that the woman, who was seated, was called the boxman, even though she was a "she". The "stick man" had a large rake-type stick which he used to move the dice and the other two men were called dealers and they handled the bets.

I went to the side of the table with, naturally, the cutest dealer. He was around thirty, black hair, brown eyes, about 5'8" or so and, best of all, he had a big smile that was just for me.

"Hi," I said. "I'm just learning to play craps and I was wondering if you could answer some questions for me."

"For you honey, anything. What do you want to know?" Glad to know that sexism isn't dead yet!

"Well, first of all, what's the difference between a come bet and a place bet? Why would anyone want to bet come when they could place any bet they want?"

"Ah," said the dealer, "a good question and from such a pretty girl!" Was he flirting with me already? "The main difference," he said, "is the 'odds' involved. When you put odds on a come bet or a pass line bet, you're paid the true odds. A place bet pays house odds. Do you know what odds are?"

"Yes," I said, and proceeded to tell him the odds of the numbers I knew by heart:

6 & 8 pay six to five (bet five dollars and get six)
4 & 10 pay two to one (bet five dollars and get ten)
5 & 9 pay three to two (bet six dollars and get nine)

"That's pretty good," he said, "only those are the true odds. Those are the payoffs you get playing pass line or come odds. But the odds on place bets are different. Place bets pay more than even money but less than true odds. What's your name, honey?"

"Uh, Tina." I replied absent mindedly. "I don't understand, why would anyone want less than true odds?"

"Tina, what a wonderful name! My name's Jack."

He paused, like he wanted me to say *'Oh, thank you, kind sir. Let's go to bed right now.'* I didn't say anything. I was concentrating on learning about odds and wasn't really interested in anything else. Besides, he was a little pushy for "off-hours". He was kind of cute, though.

"Hmm, yes. Well, you see if you place a bet you can always remove it. You can't remove a pass line or come bet. That's the main advantage to place bets. But the house odds aren't that different from true odds."

He then rattled off the house odds for the numbers I had already memorized.

6 & 8 pay seven to six (bet six dollars and get seven)
4 & 10 pay nine to five (bet five dollars and get nine)
5 & 9 pay seven to five (bet five dollars and get seven)

"Remember, these are the odds for placing a bet only. The come and pass line odds bets pay true odds. I get off in thirty minutes. Would you like to have a drink with me?"

"Uh, we'll see," I mumbled. "So, if the point is, say, a six and I have $5 on the pass line, I could also place a bet on the six, *and* have a come bet going at the same time?"

"Well, you could but you probably wouldn't want to. If you have $5 on the pass line you can bet double odds of $10. If the six wins, you'll win $17. That's $5 for your pass line bet plus $12 for your $10 odds bet, at six to five, the true odds.

"However, if you placed the six for $12, you would win $14, at seven to six odds. There is no point in making both a place and a pass or come bet. It increases your risk without increasing the reward. If you want to have more money at risk, you should bet it where you get the best odds, or where you have the flexibility of taking it down. Doing both at the same time just doesn't make too much sense. They have a real nice bar here, how about it?"

"Well . . . " I said, "what about a come bet?"

"Come bets, yes, well if the point is, say, eight, and you put $10 on the come and a six is rolled, your come bet moves to the six. Then you can take double odds on it, or $25."

"Huh," I interjected.

He explained. "In the case of the six or eight, the house allows an extra $5 which gives you a better payout and makes the accounting easier."

"Oh, I get it . . . I think."

"So, if a six rolls again before the seven, you'll win $40, $10 for the original bet, plus $30 for odds of six to five. So you can win more with the come bet, but the number has to roll twice. Its almost like playing another craps game inside of the main game. They serve really good daiquiris in the bar."

"Hmm . . . I love banana daiquiris," I said almost to myself. "Do you think we could play just a short game . . . before we go for drinks, Jack?"

"Why, sure. Joe, get the dice. We've got a virgin here!"

"Well, I'm not exactly a virgin," I said, chuckling a little.

"I'll bet," he said with a grin.

"Oh! One other thing. Do you have comp cards here?"

"Sure do," Jack said. "Player wants to be rated."

Another man came over and I filled out a short form. Then he gave me a temporary paper card.

"The next time you come back, we'll have a plastic one all ready for you," he said.

Jack smiled as the dice were pushed toward me. I put $10 on the pass line and choose two nice, friendly, winning dice. I rolled. Mr. Dice was good to me. A seven. I won $10, picked up my winnings and rolled again. This time a three rolled and I lost my bet. I put another $10 up and I rolled a six.

"Okay, so for double odds, I'll put $25 behind my pass line bet, right? Can I also place the eight for $24 and put $10 on the come? Is that OK?"

"You're doing great. What number do you want to get on the come? You should always think in advance."

"Oh," I said, "a five or nine would be fine." I rolled a five and my come bet went to the five.

"Now, I'd like to take double odds on the five - $20 right?"

"Yes. So now if you roll a five, you'll win $40 — $10 plus 3:2 odds on $20. If you roll a six you'll also win $40 — $10 plus 6:5 odds on $25. And, if you roll an eight you'll win $28 — 7:6 odds on $24."

The mists were clearing at last. A place bet is a good bet because you can choose which numbers to bet on. The come bet pays better because you have the option of making an odds bet and getting true odds, but you can't choose your number. The pass line bet seemed the best because you could bet pass before or after the point was made and you received true odds behind the line.

I rolled a five and won $40 and removed my bet. I was

scared of rolling a seven. Then I rolled an eight and won another $28. I took my bet down again and Jack mumbled something about a "grinder" but I didn't pay much attention. Then, unfortunately, a seven rolled and I lost $35 on my pass line bets. Still I came out ahead. Craps was starting to be fun again but no one was cheering and yelling. I was still the only one at the table.

"You did good," Jack said. "Want to roll again?"

"No, but I'm ready for a banana daiquiri. Where's the bar?"

He told me where the bar was and I thanked the other dealers, walked over, and waited for his shift to end. Jack was pretty cute and he did answer a lot of questions. I wondered if we would sleep together. I couldn't remember the last time I slept with a man on a friendly basis, without charging him for it. I ordered us two banana daiquiris and paid for them. Might as well thank him for his help.

Jack and the drinks arrived at the same time. They were great, made with real bananas. Jack looked different, sexier, in regular street clothes. I started the conversation by asking him how he became a dealer.

"I learned craps when I was ten or eleven, from my dad. He would organize some neighborhood games back in Pittsburgh where I was born. By the time I was 15 I was an expert player but, unless the games were rigged, I didn't win much. My dad eventually got a job as a dealer here at Binions twenty years ago, and knew Benny Binion personally. Have you seen Binions' statue outside in the back? That's him on that big iron horse. He's dead now, but my dad's still around. Doesn't play dice anymore. He's retired and travels a lot. Craps runs in my family, Mom used to play but she's dead now . . ."

"My mom is dead too," I said. "Both my parents died of

cancer."

I told him my usual white lie, the one I tell to everyone outside of my business. I said I was a singer and when he asked, I mentioned the bar I used to work in. Fortunately, he didn't know it. I didn't even know if it still existed or not.

He ordered two more rounds and I began to feel slightly tipsy. We chatted about everything in the world, like two people who have just met normally do. We didn't talk about craps at all. I don't know whether it was the daiquiris or what, but I found myself wanting to sleep with him, very much.

Finally he told me he had a room here and asked if I wanted to come up for a nightcap. I was too drunk to be coy or to wonder why a dealer had a room in the hotel but I readily agreed. How many of those drinks did I have, anyway? Four? Five?

We stumbled up to his room and I laid down on the bed, ready for action. He flopped down next to me, wrapped his arms around me and promptly fell asleep.

"Nuts," I said out loud. "What's going on here."

I was drunk, but not tired. I got up and took stock of the situation. With great difficulty, I got his clothes off. Finally, he was under the covers, naked and snoring. Should I leave, I wondered. Nah. I took off my clothes, too and snuggled in with him. He felt warm and nice.

I started touching him, using my many tricks of the trade, and it didn't take long to get at least a part of him awake. I got on top and guided him into me. It was fun, kind of like taking him against his will. A big smile crossed his face before he opened his eyes. I didn't give him a chance to say anything. Our kisses said it all. We stayed like this for a little while, with me moving back and forth, up and down, until he gently rolled me over and took control. I had already worked myself close to coming, and when he started pumping me harder and harder, it didn't take long at all. He came almost immediately afterwards, then he melted on top of me and fell asleep again. This time I was content to let him be. I cuddled up against him and fell sound asleep.

I guess I found a new method of turning a soft six into a hard one!

April

I didn't see Jack again for a while. I was sure he was married. There was also something odd about him that I just couldn't put my finger on.

March quickly turned into April, a big month for Las Vegas. The National Association of Broadcasters is here. And, best of all, families start coming again. It's not too hot and not too cold, and the pools begin to open toward the end of the month.

Whenever I had a free hour or two I would go to different casinos and get comp cards. I found that some casinos had two different cards, one for table games and one for slots. I applied for them all figuring that I had nothing to lose and maybe a free meal to gain. It was nice to know that if I played craps for an hour or two, I'd get a free dinner and drinks, sometimes worth as much as $50! I also got on all the mailing lists and received lots of offers for discounted meals and rooms. Sometimes the rooms were even offered free during the week. I almost wished that I was a visitor instead of a local so I could take advantage of all the free stuff.

One day, I found myself in the downtown mall and decided to stop in at Binions, just to look around. No particular reason, of course. I went to the craps tables and there was Jack.

I caught his eye and he yelled, "Hi, Tina."

"Hi, Jack, just thought I'd shoot a little craps."

"Well, you're always welcome here," he said.

I gave him my comp card, which he gave to someone else.

Then I got it back a few minutes later and stashed it in my purse. I cashed in for $200 and bet $5 on the pass line. The existing point was eight.

"How long have you been married?" I asked him suddenly. He looked incredulous. "How did you know?" he gasped.

"Oh, I have a way of knowing these things. I don't mind, really. Do you live here in Vegas?"

"No, we live in Elko. When I deal here, the manager gives me a temporary room, the one we were in. I guess because they all remember my dad. He lives with us. We all live together, Dad, my, uh, wife Jane, my son Steve, and me."

The shooter rolled a six. I put $10 odds behind my pass line bet. "Gee I would think you would live a little better, with both you and your dad being dealers. Don't dealers make a lot of money?"

"Are you kidding? Most of us make minimum wage, plus tips."

The shooter rolled a ten. Then an eight. I had won! "Tips? How do dealers get tips? Am I supposed to leave a dollar on the table or something?"

I know this sounded crass but I was really curious and didn't know how else to say it.

"Well, there are quite a few ways, actually. Sometimes, when a player is finished, he gives us a tip, like a $5 chip. 'For the dealers', he says. Someone else might place a bet for us. A "Two-Way" bet is one for the player and one for the dealer. You could bet, for example, a "two-way hard eight". Then if you win, the dealer wins. Usually, if we get tips, we're encouraged to help the player more. Actually, if a player wins a lot, he would tip us anyway, so we really benefit more if the player wins than if the house wins."

The same shooter was about to shoot. "Okay," I said, putting two chips side by side, on the pass line, "One for the dealer."

"Dealer on the line," Jack said aloud.

I asked "If you don't make that much, why don't you become a professional craps player? You seem to really know the game."

"Oh, eh, I tried that, eh, once," Jack said. "While I was single it was OK. But sometimes I would drop a few hundred and couldn't pay the rent. Other times I'd be a few thousand ahead and I'd be on top of the world."

The point was ten. Fat Chance. Jack asked, "You married?"

"Me, nope. Still searching for Mr. Right." A ten point, ugh. Wish I could figure out a way in advance what the point would be. Then, if it was a six or eight, I would bet pass line with odds. With a four or ten I would bet don't pass with odds. I started thinking about that. There must be a way to choose pass or don't pass in advance.

The very next roll was a seven. Ugh. We both lost. I hate fours and tens. The dealers thanked me anyway.

"Look, Jack, I have to go. I have an appointment. I just stopped by to say hi." I cashed out my chips.

"OK, Tina. Listen, you know where I work. Drop by again sometime. I really enjoyed, uh, talking to you. Maybe we can do it again sometime."

"OK, Jack maybe I will. Hey, smile a little. It's not the end of the world. I won't tell anybody if you don't and we had some fun together. Let's leave it at that."

"OK, Tina, bye and take care of yourself."

"Bye, Jack." We kissed, just a peck, and I left. I walked through Binions toward the parking lot, but then I remembered something. I stopped a cocktail waitress and asked her where the statue of Benny Binion was. I walked behind the casino and found it in the at the edge of the parking lot, next to the sidewalk. It's a giant statue of a cowboy on a horse. So this was the man who started it all. May you rest in peace, Benny.

I got into my red Mustang convertible and drove home. I had a quick shower and Jack was washed out of my hair. Oh well, I wasn't looking for a husband anyway. Think positively, whispered Dad's voice in my head. I had learned a lot about craps and maybe found a new friend.

I was thinking about betting pass and don't pass at the same time when that blinking red light caught my eye. My answering machine was full of messages including a client for the night. He had asked for me specifically and was paying for extra services which could mean anything from S & M to watching me touch myself. Oh well, money is money. I decided to forgo casino hopping and took a nap. When I woke up, the digital clock on the nightstand said 5:00 pm. Since I didn't have to be at the Aladdin until 8:00, I had plenty of time.

I roamed around my condo for a few minutes, feeling good and at peace with the world. I didn't entertain a whole lot, still don't for that matter, and never brought clients home, so I didn't feel the need to spend a lot of money on interior decoration. My things are comfortable and homey, but certainly not fancy. I have always saved my money and my expenses were mostly for clothes, hair and nails, things like that, to keep up appearances. My condo is a fairly large one bedroom, with a roomy kitchen and a big bathroom. Everything is done in muted ocean colors, pale greens and blues, with a little rose thrown in for contrast. There is an eclectic collection of mementos but no real clutter. At that time in my life, it just felt like home - warm and cozy.

My stomach moved me to the kitchen where I nuked a TV dinner and sat at the table looking out on the quiet afternoon street life of my residential neighborhood. After straightening up the kitchen, I headed for the bathroom with visions of a nice, leisurely bath. By the time I had finished soaking, I felt terrific. I looked at myself in my full length mirror as I toweled dry and appraised what I saw - a pretty good body, nice firm breasts, and long brown hair. Looking pretty good for pushing 30, I thought. Still naked, I put on a little foundation, checking closely for complexion problems. I was very lucky and had inherited great genes from my mother. My skin was still firm and moist, with just a hint of tiny lines around the eyes. I added eye makeup, something smokey for glamour, and was finished. My closet produced a body hugging slip dress in red and I rummaged in my lingerie drawer until I found the matching set of garters, bra, and panties. The lady in red, sexy enough to warrant my customer's Big Bucks. I hopped in my car and headed toward the strip.

The Aladdin Hotel should be a lot better than it is. It's large, has a good location, and some good shows. But for some reason it just never quite caught on. It has a really large Performing Arts Showroom, but a dinky embarrassing coffee shop type buffet. I guess a lot of people come to see the shows and then take their gambling money elsewhere. It's never crowded and, worst of all, only has two craps tables. Oh, well. I finished looking around and at 7:45 went up to the appointed room.

I knocked and was let in by a man who must have been eighty if he was a day.

"You must be Tina," he said.

"Yes. I'm sorry, I'm a little early."

"That's quite all right. Come in. Would you like a drink?"

"Uh, sure. Kahlua and coke?"

"Yes, yes. Please sit down."

I sat. He was in a lavish suite, one I never knew they had

at the Aladdin. He must have been a really high roller. There were three large rooms and I could see a large screen TV and a Jacuzzi in the background.

"Here's your drink, young lady. We are expecting someone else, who should be here shortly. Please be patient. And, don't worry, you will be well paid."

Given his age, I wasn't particularly worried, although some of my working girl friends think I'm awfully naive. We sat in silence for a few minutes and I thought I had figured out a plan to play craps betting the pass line and the don't pass at the same time. Nothing like concentrating on your work. The doorbell interrupted my thoughts. In walked a beautiful black woman wearing a gorgeous purple gown, with high, high spiked heels. She was much taller than I was, probably 5'11" or so in her heels. Her breasts were enormous and when she saw me, she smiled broadly.

"So this is the one, huh," she said to "Mr. Jones".

"Yes, yes she is," he answered. "Well, Tina, I called your service and requested they send me a beautiful woman who had never made love to another woman before. They made a wise choice. That's what I want the two of you to do, make love while I watch, that's all."

Gee, I felt honored. This black woman was gorgeous! Only thing was, I had been in numerous threesomes before and the service knew it. I guess they thought I was a good actress.

"What's your name?" I asked the Amazon.

"You can call me Pearl, honey . . . and you're Tina?"

"That's right," I said as she came over and sat next to me. She caressed my cheek and winked at me.

"Don't be nervous, honey, I won't hurt you," she said aloud.

I winked back. We both knew that everyone in our profession is a little bisexual or at least considers it part of the job when required. "Oh," I said, "It's just that I've never done this before." This was fun.

She caressed my neck and then kissed me lightly on the lips. "Haven't I seen you before?" she whispered to me.

"Could be," I whispered back.

"Let's go into the bedroom," she said, aloud.

The bedroom was enormous. It had a four-poster bed with a mirror on the ceiling. Mr. Jones followed us in and sat at the foot of the bed, watching, just watching.

I let Pearl lead me to the bed and gently push me down on my back. I felt my skirt rising up on my thighs and scooted around a little to help it along. Pearl began running her hands slowly along my body, kissing me, our tongues entwining. "Please, oh, please, oh, I don't know what to do," I said aloud. Maybe Mr. Jones was turned on by my upcoming deflowering. I kept sneaking looks at him but he just sat there.

Pearl slipped my red dress over my head in one motion to reveal my red garters, bra, and panties. She kept moving me around so Mr. Jones could get a good view of everything. I had been around, but she *really* knew what she was doing! Then she took off her own dress, very slowly, to reveal her own set of matching lingerie. I was pretty worked up by then, watching and pretending to be shy. It was all I could do to keep still, remembering I was still a virgin.

"What do I do now?" I pleaded. "Please help me." Pearl removed my bra and licked and nibbled my already hard nipples. She slowly slipped off my silk stockings, then removed my garters and panties. She started rubbing her body ferociously on mine, kissing me vigorously and I began responding in kind.

"You've done this before," she whispered in my ear.

"Maybe just a little," I whispered back, as my hand reached down into her wet panties.

"Well, my little girl," she said loud enough for Mr. Jones to hear. "I'm going to teach you how to make love to a woman. From now on you will call me 'Mistress Pearl' and do everything I say. Understand?"

"Yes, Mistress Pearl," I said. She *forced* me to remove her bra and suck on her waiting nipples. She had wonderful, large brown breasts, with huge nipples that were erect and hard. Then I was *forced* to remove her stockings, garter belt and panties. She maneuvered me around so I was directly in front of Mr. Jones and continued touching and caressing and licking every part of me. I was a good student and we quickly brought each other to orgasm. All this time Mr. Jones was just sitting there watching.

Out of nowhere she produced a vibrator and turned it on. She was about to play with it but suddenly Mr. Jones said, "That's enough, please leave now!"

I looked at Pearl and she motioned me to leave. We both got up, found our clothes, and quickly left the bedroom. Pearl closed the door. "Let's go honey. We're done and you did really well." We put our clothes on.

"What's going on?" I asked as we dressed.

"Who knows? This happens every time. Easiest money I ever made. This is my fifth time with Mr. Jones. Hope he lives forever."

"What is he doing in there?" I asked.

"Don't know, don't care, just as long as we get paid. Mr. Jones pays our services directly. He must be pretty important."

She looked at me, right in my eyes. "You're pretty cute you know."

"And you are gorgeous!" I replied enthusiastically. "Such a wonderful body and terrific breasts." She came over and we kissed, long and hard.

"Maybe we can get together later. What service are you on?"

I told her and we exchanged service numbers, and our private ones as well.

"Oh, by the way," she said, "my name is Yvonne, what's yours?"

"Tina. Tina is my real name."

"Well, what do you know! Good to meet you, Tina! I'm sure I'll be seeing more of you in the future!"

Had I known the truth of Yvonne's statement, I would have paid a lot more attention to the moment.

We walked out together but she left so quickly that I forgot to ask her if she played craps!

I felt pretty good, having just made $500 for twenty minutes of pleasant work. But the craps tables beckoned.

I went back inside the casino and found the tables. I was the only one there and only one table was open, with just a $1 minimum bet. I guess the Aladdin doesn't cater much to craps players.

I had an idea I wanted to test, though, and an empty table seemed perfect for it. No players or dealers would complain if I were the only one there. I walked up to the table.

"Hi, guys! Mind if I try a new system out on your table?"

They all fell over themselves in welcoming me. Not only was I very provocatively dressed, I was a real paying customer.

"Do anything you want, honey!" one said.

Isn't sexism wonderful! "Oh, can I get a comp card?"

They seemed surprised. Apparently they don't get too many requests for rated players. We filled out the necessary form and I was on my way to getting yet another comp card. I proceeded to bet $5 on the pass line and $5 on the don't pass. I figured if a six or eight rolled I would take odds on the pass line bet and remove my don't pass bet. If a four or ten rolled I would take odds on don't pass. Unfortunately, you can't take down your pass line bet. For a five or nine I would take the don't pass down but place no odds on the pass line.

As luck would have it, a twelve rolled. I lost the pass but didn't win on the don't pass. "Have to play the twelve if you're going to do that," one of the dealers said. Why didn't he tell me before? Oh, well. I put $1 on the twelve, which was a one roll bet but paid thirty to one.

I rolled the dice. A six! I put $10 in odds behind the pass line and removed the don't pass bet. I hardly noticed that I also lost the $1 on the twelve. A few rolls later a six rolled and I had $17.

Now, I bet $10 pass and $10 don't pass. This time I rolled a five point and removed my don't pass. The five rolled, so I won another $10!

I bet $5 pass and don't pass the next time, and the point was a four, so I put $10 odds behind my don't pass. A few rolls later I rolled a seven and won on the don't pass but lost the pass bet, giving me a profit of $5.

The dealers told me I could lay the four or ten, but then I would have to pay a house commission, or "vig" (vigorish) of 5% on the possible win, usually with a $1 minimum. This meant if I laid $20 against the four, for example, I would have to pay the house $1, and if I won, at 1:2 odds, I would only win $10. On the don't pass line if I bet $20 I would win $20. Of course, after my experience at T.I., I was *thoroughly* familiar with laying bets against the four or ten.

I played my new pass/don't pass method for perhaps half an hour and it seemed to work fine. I was ahead $60, not exactly a fortune, but it occurred to me if I were betting $25 instead of $5 I would be ahead a lot more. By this time, I was totally bored. It was the same thing all the time with no variety

and I *really* like variety. Plus, I was the only shooter. Boring!
At least I had found a safe and easy way to play, and make a
little money at the same time.

I got tired, left, and went home. On my answering machine
was a call from Yvonne. I called her immediately but she was
out, so I left a message.

Too bad I couldn't lay her instead of the fours and tens!

May

May has three big events, the Council of Shopping Centers, the Seniors Classic Golf Tournament, and the Helldorado Rodeo and Carnival. The Big Event in May for me, however, was Big Red. We met through my service, as usual and once I laid eyes on him, I sure was glad that all he wanted was oral gratification. He was big in *every* sense of the word, 6'4" or so, red hair, red beard, and he must have weighed about 300 pounds. He was staying at the MGM Grand, the biggest casino there is.

I went there early for my 1:00 pm appointment with Big Red, to have lunch at one of their many restaurants. There are more than twenty of them, as well as animated characters from The Wizard of Oz, and a giant theme park like a mini-Disneyland. You can walk for a mile inside the MGM and never cross the same path twice.

Now I, along with other equally sophisticated craps players, don't like the term Big Red. This means a seven, and after the point a seven loses for almost everyone. But not for Big Red, as I later found out.

His hotel room was enormous, much bigger than my condo. It had at least three rooms, but I only got to see one, the bedroom. Fortunately I was only there for four or five minutes. I didn't even have to take off my clothes. Easy money. As I was preparing to leave, he said, "Want to learn how to play craps with me?"

I was stunned. "With a name like Big Red I never would have thought you played craps."

"Ha! That's what you think! Come along and learn how the real men play!"

Now, how could I pass up an invitation like that? I thought that I would keep quiet about already knowing something about the game. If he wanted me to be a virgin though, I would have to say something. I didn't want to bring him bad luck.

We went downstairs to the casinos of the MGM Grand. There are actually three of them; the Hollywood casino ($5 minimum bets), Emerald City ($10 minimum bets) and the Monte Carlo ($20 minimum bets).

We, of course, went to Monte Carlo. He ambled up to a semi-crowded table and said in a loud voice, "Now I'll show you how to play *real* craps!" The point, as luck would have it, was four.

"Lay $100 no four!"

A few rolls later a seven rolled and he had won about $50.

"Ha! That's why they call me BIIIIGG RED!"

A few players left the table. Most people don't like don't bettors.

The next point was eight. He said "$100 no-four and $100 no-ten." The very next roll was an eight. People looked at him and snickered. But his bets stayed up and he didn't lose anything. The first come out roll was, of course, a seven. He had won about $100.

He guffawed and laughed. "BIIIIGG RED strikes again!" More people left the table.

At this point, I started to see what he was doing. He was owning the table. Everyone still there was playing either against him or not at all. It had turned into a game of Big Red. He was intimidating everyone, including me. I was literally afraid to place a pass line bet.

This time he was the shooter. He rolled a three. Everyone

on the pass line lost and he laughed at them! He was really obnoxious! He had don't bets on the four and ten.

"OK," he said, "$120 on the no-nine."

He rolled a six. People bet on the pass line. The six won and some very small snickers were heard. Then on the come out another six hit, which also won. He still had his three don't bets up. Now, of all things, he rolled a ten. He had lost $100. Everyone applauded! Not to be outdone, he roared, "$500 on the no-ten!" The table was silent. He rolled a five. A six. An eight. And a seven. He had won about $380 on one roll of the dice, and was now almost $1000 ahead. Everyone else left the table. He started laughing uproariously! I felt sick. He was a craps bully. I started to leave, too.

"Hey, Tina! Don't go! Hey! Let me buy you a drink! Hey!"

I started walking away.

"Tina, wait. Have a drink with me. I'll tell you something no one else will tell you about playing craps." He said this quietly, seriously. I figured I didn't have anything to lose.

We went to one of the fancier bars and ordered two strawberry daiquiris (they didn't have banana) and he explained.

"Look, when you play craps, you have to control the table. Your mind has to control the dice, the other players, the dealers, everything. It's like a game of chess. You have to really know and understand all the players and figure out what they might do next. I've known some players who can do this by hard concentrating. I can't. I do it by being a bastard. It doesn't matter whether I play do or don't. If I come to a table and see that someone else is in control, I leave. If I'm in control, I win. If I'm not, I lose."

He said all this in a quiet, studious voice. Was all that Big Red stuff really an act? Could he really control the dice?

"When I started playing," he said, "I noticed that some players won all the time and some lost all the time. The people who lost just weren't confident. They didn't know all the rules and just threw their money away. The confident players succeeded, because they knew they would win. I wanted to be like them. It was difficult for me because I really stood out in a crowd. People stared at me. I was different. I decided to turn my size into an advantage. I became a don't better. The odds, after the come out, are in favor of the don't better anyway."

I couldn't believe it. In the space of a few minutes this man had turned from an obnoxious beast into a caring individual who was sharing his life with me.

"I called myself BIG RED because I was big and had red hair. That the seven was called Big Red was just a bonus. I wanted to inject myself into everyone's playing and shatter their confidence. I knew I would win in those circumstances."

Wow, another whole new angle to craps. He believed he would win, and so he did. I ventured a question. "But, how did you become that confident?"

"I read everything I could on craps. There's not a book or software program on craps that I don't have. Craps became a passion for me. With knowledge came confidence. Of course, this took quite a few years. There are more than 100 books on craps and I've read, no, studied them all."

"But couldn't you do this without being Big Red? What was your name before?"

"Uh, well . . . my real name is Marvin."

"Marvin?"

"Doesn't exactly inspire confidence does it? I know, there're a lot of famous Marvins, but as a kid everyone called me Marvie and I grew up to hate the name. I thought that if I changed my name I'd change my life. And I did."

I thought for a second. That's what all the really successful people have in common, confidence. They all know they will succeed. If they fail once, they treat it as a learning experience and just keep on trying. They know they will triumph. Maybe this would work for me, although the thought of studying 100 books on craps wasn't especially appealing.

"Most people play craps for fun. They really don't know how to play. Say, have you ever *really* wanted to do something?"

"Me? Oh, I've always wanted to be a singer."

"Well, if you're a *good* singer, don't you have to practice every day? Don't you study how other people sing? The people who are successful singers didn't get there by luck, they studied hard, worked hard, and they *knew* they would triumph. Most people take the easy way out and wait for breaks or luck. I make my own luck. This world is a wonderful, fabulous place, with lots of opportunities. Anyone can do anything they want to, if they put their mind in gear and *just do it*!"

I thought for a second. "I guess that's true. In my profession all us girls are deathly afraid of gaining weight. It used to be very hard for me at first. I wanted to eat everything. But my livelihood depends on my staying slim and trim, so I force myself to eat fruits and salads all the time. Maybe its not as, uh, determined as your goals are, but it worked for me. You know, you could do that, too. I bet with your mind control you could get under 200 pounds easy. Maybe then you'll have even more confidence and could stop bullying people at the craps table."

I guess I was a little too blunt because he just sat there, staring.

"I never thought of that before, Tina. You might just have a good idea there. Thanks for being so honest with me."

I was about to say something else when I was distracted by a glimpse of Jack, the dealer from Binions, walking past. I wondered what was he doing there at the MGM Grand. I watched him and he walked straight to the craps tables and started playing.

"Something wrong?" asked B.R.

"No, no, I just saw someone I know. Would you mind if I went and said hello to him?"

"No, not at all," said Marvin/Big Red. "I have to be going anyway. Say Tina, would you mind if I called you again sometime?"

"Marv," I said smiling, "you can call me anytime you want."

We parted and I walked over to the craps table, but Jack was gone. I found a friendly looking dealer and asked, "Excuse me, but I'm looking for a friend of mine, Jack, who was playing here a few minutes ago."

"Yeah," the dealer said, "Jack, sure we know him. Comes in here every few days. Wins a little, but mostly loses. This time he lost $500 in a few minutes and then split. If he comes back, who can I say is looking for him?"

"Oh, that's OK, I'll just call him at home." I walked away, thinking, what's going on with Jack? He's here every few days and plays with $500? What was he doing? Where did he get the money?

Suddenly I remembered Big Red and walked back to the bar where we had been sitting, but he was gone, too.

I decided to play a little craps at the Hollywood tables. I bought in for $300 and gave them my comp card. I was building up quite a collection of those little pieces of plastic.

While I was getting my chips, I studied the players. There were six of them, four men and two women. The two women were alone and in their sixties. I imagined the one on the left to be married, with her husband at a convention. The one on the right was single and man-hungry. The first man was married, but had one, no two mistresses. The second man looked confident like he probably came here every month. He was the one I had to beat. I watched and he was playing the pass line with two come bets. The third and forth men were young, and I imagined them to be gay lovers. They were just here to have fun.

I caught the eye of man #2 and then looked away, discreetly touching my breast. He saw my move and I could tell he was flustered. The last point, a six, sevened out, so I decided to bet the don't pass with $20.

"Twenty dollars on the don't pass," I said loudly, trying my best to act like Big Red. The point was an eight. I smiled broadly and said aloud, "Great, I always win on the eight!"

Sure enough, the very next roll was a seven. Maybe Big Red was right. I stayed on the don't pass and the next point was a ten. Everyone groaned and I smiled at everyone in turn, thinking of the stories I had made up for them. This was fun!

However as luck would have it, a few rolls later, the ten rolled. I laughed out loud! "Great! Lay the ten for $40!" Everyone gasped and the gay lovers left. The first come out roll was a seven. I was exhilarated, but didn't want to play any more. Fortunately everyone else left. People just don't like rowdy don't bettors, especially if they're winning.

I just can't understand why they all didn't switch to the don't side with me. If a table is hot, pass line bets are great, but when a table is cold, why not bet the don't side? Craps players should be willing and able to switch back and forth, according to table conditions, but not many of them do.

I left and drove toward home. Confidence. That's all anyone needs to succeed! And you get confidence by learning and studying. And you learn by reading and applying what you read to real-life situations. I needed to get some more craps books. I drove to the Gamblers Book Club on 11th Street and found four new ones. I drove home and read all four of them. Confidence! That's all anyone needs to succeed, and I was going to get it!

June

June is one of the hottest months of the year in Las Vegas and has no major holidays or conventions. The hotels have lots of room specials this month, some for as low as $5. In June, you need a hotel with a good swimming pool and my favorite pool is at the Tropicana.

I had an appointment at the Trop, with a new customer, so I went early to explore the craps tables in the casino. The Trop is replete with real talking birds, monkeys and all sorts of wildlife throughout. To my surprise and delight they also had a temporary special promotion at the craps tables. If you rolled three elevens in a row you could win $5000!

Anyway, my date was in the Tower, near their Convention Center. His room had a mirror on the ceiling, something I've never seen before at the Trop. The date was uneventful, he didn't play craps, and I never saw him again. After we were finished, I went downstairs wanting to try my hand at winning $5000. I was sure that Big Red could do it, no problem.

I played for a while but three elevens never came up. Since it only cost $1 to bet the elevens, I figured I could bet 5000 times before I lost any money. After losing only $10, I realized how ridiculous this was. I stopped for a minute and noticed a cute guy playing weirdly. He was betting against the four and ten, then taking them down, and betting on the same numbers he had bet against on the don't pass. It didn't make any sense at all, but he seemed to be winning. Soon, he counted his chips, smiled, and cashed out. I followed him up the escalator into one of the upstairs bars with a view of the pool's waterfall. He sat down and ordered a drink.

"Hi, mind if I join you?" He looked confused but shrugged his shoulders. "I was watching you play craps downstairs and I was wondering if you could help me?"

Another shoulder shrug. Talkative guy, this one. "I'm just starting to learn about craps and was wondering about your playing methods. You seemed to be betting against yourself. Could you please tell me what you were doing?"

He thought for a second and said, "I wasn't betting against myself, I was just making "insurance" bets."

"Insurance? I don't understand."

"Well," he said, "do you know about don't bets?"

"A little."

"Well, if you bet, say, the don't four . . . "

"I know you can bet on the hard four as insurance, right?"

"Well, yes, you can do that. But you still can lose your bet when a soft four rolls. If you bet on the don't four *and* the do four, you'll never lose."

"Well, that's true, the bets will cancel out. You won't lose but you won't win either."

"That's not necessarily true. Do you know that the odds are different for a don't four and a do four?"

Hmm, I thought for a few seconds. "Doesn't the do four pay one-to-two — bet ten get twenty — on pass line and come odds? And the don't four pays two-to-one — bet $20, get ten — on don't pass and don't come odds. So they cancel out, right?"

"Well, that's true, but a place bet on the four or ten pays nine-to-five. And, if you lay the four or ten you have to pay a 5% vig. You can also "buy" a number any time for a 5% vig and get full odds. For example I can buy the four for a dollar and get full odds of two to one instead of nine to five."

"Okay, believe it or not, I am following all this. But, so

what? Is this part of your system?"

"Yes. If, for example, I have $50 on the don't pass line and a four becomes the point, I immediately buy the four for $30 plus the $3 vig. This way if the seven rolls I win my $50 don't pass and lose my $33 buy bet, giving me a $17 profit.

"But, if the four does roll I win $60 at two-to-one true odds on my buy bet, but lose my $50 don't pass bet, plus the $3 vig. So, I always win either $7 or $17, when the four or ten is the point. And, since the seven rolls three times as much as the four or the ten, I usually win $17 most of the time."

My head was reeling. A winner every time? There had to be something wrong with this somewhere . . . I know . . .

"Yes, I know what you're thinking. This only happens after the point is made. Before that I'm very vulnerable to losing my $50 on the don't pass. If a seven rolls, I lose. So I have insurance there also. On the come-out, I lay the four and ten for $60 each. If a seven rolls, I lose $50 from the don't pass and win $60 from the lay bets. I would actually win only $57 because $3 (5% of the winnings) goes to the house vig. So, if a seven rolls, I'm still $7 ahead. Then, after the point is made, I remove the don't bets on the four and ten."

"That certainly does sound like a good system," I said, "but my old system was similar in that I laid the four and ten along with their respective hard ways. Someone rolled five soft fours and tens in between sevens. Couldn't the same thing happen to you? If the first point is a four or a ten you'll lose your $60 insurance bet."

"That's very true. And it has happened to me in the past, unfortunately. But the chances of a four or ten rolling are really only three out of thirty-six, or one in twelve, and a lot higher at certain times, like on three successive come out rolls. And, if the four or ten is the point, I'll lay two times odds on my $50 don't pass and win $100 if the shooter sevens out. Of course, I can make an insurance bet by buying the four or ten and/or betting on the hard four or ten. By the way, what's your name?"

"Oh, eh, Tina. But what if someone does roll a combination of fours and tens on, say, five successive rolls? Then what? All your winnings would be wiped out."

"No they wouldn't, because of my money management system. My goal is to either win $120 or lose $120, unless I'm testing a system. But, if I'm just playing for fun, I leave the table when I've won $120. And, if I lose $120 I also leave the table. This way my losses are limited. I've won $120 many more times than I've lost. Sometimes I'd be on a roll and there are no fours and tens rolling at all. I'd count up my chips and have $200 or so. I'd still leave the table. Money management is *the* most important thing in craps. By the way, my name is Steve."

"Oh. Yes. Well, glad to meet you, Steve." I was still thinking this all over.

"It's getting late," Steve said. "Uh, would you like to have dinner with me? There's a terrific restaurant across the street at the Luxor. Want to give it a try?"

"Sure," I said, still thinking. This guy must really know how to play.

We went downstairs and passed the craps tables. "Hey," he said. "Why don't I show you my system again and we'll make a quick $120!"

"Okay." He bought in for $500 and gave his comp card to the pit boss. I just wanted to watch. He laid the four and ten for $60 each and put $50 on the don't Pass and $3 on the Yo to protect himself from losing on the eleven on the come out.

As luck would have it, the first point was four. He was down $60, because he lost his no-four. He then bought the four for $30. The seven rolled so he had won $50 from the don't pass, and lost $30 plus his original $60. He was down $40.

He tried it again, and unfortunately, the point was ten. He lost another $60, but a few rolls later the shooter sevened out and Steve won. He laid the four and ten two more times and removed them, leaving up his $50 don't pass bet. He won both times and was ahead by almost $100.

"Let's stop," he said. "I have a feeling and I always go by my feelings."

He cashed out and we walked across the overhead walkway, past the Excalibur, to the Luxor.

I had been to the Luxor quite a few times, with its Sphinx out in front, and its light and water shows illuminating the grounds. It is supposed to be a huge archeological dig, complete with mysteries and treasures. It has an Egyptian museum, including a replica of King Tut's tomb, and one of the best ride simulations around. There is also a River Nile inside of the hotel which has boats running every few minutes. All this sounds great, but it's aimed toward families with children, not single craps-playing people like myself.

The Isis restaurant was a great surprise! It was very elegant, with terrific food, probably one of the best restaurants I've ever been to. But the best thing of all was Steve. I wish I could have recorded that first date.

Steve was 5'8", medium length brown hair, about thirty-five and, most important, single. He's a writer with three computer books under his belt. I told him I was a dancer at a downtown club, which turned out later to be a terrible mistake, but I had no way of knowing that at the time.

We ate and talked. He lived alone in San Diego and traveled a lot. He was single. He was working on a novel. He was single. He loved mathematical games and, of course, craps. He was single. By the time dessert came, I was in love.

Well, in lust anyway.

"What got you interested in craps?" I asked him.

"Well, I was always interested in chance and probability. I was drawn to Las Vegas because of its glamour and promise of easy money, and to craps because of its complicated rules. Even before I placed my first bet, I read all I could on craps, and bought a good computer simulation game called 'Beat The House'. I practiced a lot. I played a lot and I lost a lot. I started to understand that to win, one has to understand this game totally. And, most of all, one has to be able to switch strategies, sometimes in the middle of a game."

Steve had beautiful green eyes!

"Soon I was able to win almost constantly, using a variety of methods. Do you know what a comp is?"

I reached into my purse and took out my eleven comp cards.

"I guess you do," he said, smiling. He has such a wonderful smile. "Comps are a big bonus to any player who can just break even. Some of the casinos not only give me room, food and beverage, but airline refunds as well. And I don't *just* break even, most of the time. I'm now pretty confident that I can win between $100 and $200 per session. If I play for three days, I usually go home with around $1000 and get a free vacation as well!"

Confidence, he had confidence. I asked, "You sound very knowledgeable about this. Ever thought of doing it full time?"

"Yes," he said, "I think everyone who has ever played craps has thought of it. But I like writing. Craps is just a hobby, and I think I'll lose interest if it turns into a business. Maybe when I retire I'll move here and play every weekend. But for now, I just come here once a month or so. The extra money really helps and there's no pressure to make a living at it."

Once he had a drink in him, he really started talking. He said he had been divorced twice and I could see there was a lot of pain in his eyes when he talked about it. He seemed like a wonderful man and I really wanted to be with him.

However, when we finished eating, he didn't invite me back to the Trop where he was staying. I boldly invited him to my place for a drink but he declined. I thought he was probably just too tired. We did make a date for dinner the next day, same place, at 8:00 pm. He went back to the Trop and I went back to my condo, both of us sleeping alone and hungry for affection.

The next day I went to the Gamblers Book Store and found two new craps books. Then, at the Gamblers General store on Main Street, I found a small, used craps table for $50. At home I read both books and then played craps with myself for about an hour. I was getting a little tired of hooking and was thinking of becoming a legitimate dancer again. I had started wondering what would I do when I was forty and I needed to find something else to do, now. I thought of Steve. I did tell him I was a dancer. It would be nice if I really was one. This was his last day in Vegas until the following month and I couldn't wait to see him at the Luxor.

The day dragged on until 7:00 pm arrived. I had dressed in a somewhat conservative green chiffon outfit, medium cleavage, swing skirt and black patent strappy heels. I drove to the Luxor and got there at 7:30, half an hour early. Steve wasn't at the Isis so I decided to go downstairs and watch the craps tables. Sometimes I just like to watch other players, to see if they have a winning system, and then figure out what it is.

When I got there, I got the surprise of my life. Jack, my teacher from Binions, was there. He was betting and losing heavily. I was standing unobtrusively at an adjoining table and he didn't see me. He got mad every time he lost. I was staring at him when someone put his hand on my shoulder.

"Hi, Tina, thought I'd find you here." It was Steve. "I got here a little early and you weren't at the restaurant, so I came down here."

"I checked at the restaurant for you, too. I decided to come down here and watch how other people play."

"Learn anything?"

"Nope. Want to go to dinner?" I looked around and Jack was gone.

"Sure," he said, "let's go!"

We took the elevator up to Isis and were seated by the Maitre 'D. We made small talk and ordered.

"Look," Steve said, "I want to explain something. Last night I had a lot of fun talking with you. You're very intelligent and outgoing. But, I've been divorced twice. My second divorce isn't even final yet and I'm kind of scared of new relationships. It was so easy to talk to you because we talked about craps, but when the dinner ended, I didn't know what to do. A few years ago I would have invited you up to my room, but now, I don't know. And when you invited me back to your place, I was confused. Does any of this make sense?"

"Yes," I said, my heart beating wildly. "I didn't quite know what to do, either." Which was true. I guess having sex is a little less serious to me than it is to most people.

"Great," he said, starting on the appetizer. "I suppose honesty *is* the best policy . . ."

I winced. Should I tell him? No. He probably wouldn't want to see me again.

" . . . and the truth is, I really wanted to invite you up to my room last night, but I was afraid. I'm much more comfortable talking about craps. I guess I'm afraid of getting into a new relationship right now."

I gulped. Maybe I should tell him. "Well, to be honest, I wanted to go up to your room too . . ."

I just couldn't do it. "We do seem to have a lot in common and I liked talking to you. I know how you feel about your marriages, it must have been rough. Any alimony or problems?"

"No, I pretty much gave my ex-wives what they wanted, and they both have good jobs, so they treated me fairly too. But what hurt the most is that I couldn't figure out how to save the marriages. I'm usually very analytical about everything and I have this feeling of utter failure."

He was a few inches from me when he said that and, on impulse, I reached out and hugged him to me. "There. Sometimes all people need are good hugs." He looked at me and smiled. I thought he was going to kiss me but just then the waiter appeared with our entrees and we separated.

"Tina, how did you ever get interested in craps? It's so unusual to see someone so interested in the game."

Another opening for me. "Well, I, uh, one of my girlfriends introduced it to me." Brave and honest, that's me.

We ate for a while and both had Keoki Coffee for dessert.

"Now what?" Steve said.

"Tell you what. I have a small craps table at home . . ."

"Really, you have your own craps table?"

"Yes, well it's a small one, actually, but it works. What do you say we go to my place and play some craps?"

He paused for just a second and said, "OK."

We left Isis and he followed me to my condo. When we arrived, he made the usual polite comments about how nice it was. He sat down at the kitchen table where my craps table was, and I offered him a drink.

"Do you have Kahlua and coke?" he asked as my eyes

widened in amazement. He was the only person I'd ever known, other than myself, who likes that unique combination.

"I like that drink, too," I said chuckling. I made us both tall ones and we got down to business.

Steve played his no-four/no-ten system and I played a simple system, placing the sixes and eights. I placed $30 each on the six and eight after the come out and, after one hit, I took them both down. At the end of an hour, Steve was ahead $160 and I was ahead $150. We had also each consumed three tall Kahlua and cokes and we started making silly bets.

Soon we were down to zero again. "Just goes to show, you should never drink while you're playing craps," Steve said.

"Look," I said, "It's late. You can stay here and sleep on the couch. I know you have a plane to catch tomorrow. Don't worry, I won't be offended."

"OK, Tina, thanks. Can I see you next month when I'm here again?"

"Absolutely! What time do you leave tomorrow? I'll set the alarm and make sure you wake up on time." We set the alarm clock near my bed for 8:00 am. He curled up on the couch with a spare blanket and I went into my bedroom, alone, and closed the door. Oh, well. I took off my clothes, turned off the light, and got into bed.

A few minutes later, I heard a slight noise and the bedroom door opened. Steve walked in, naked. As he looked down at me I opened the covers for him and he slid in, hugging and kissing me. We held each other tight, not wanting to let go. He felt wonderful! We made love slowly and gently, as though we had been doing it for years. We seemed to be made for each other. Afterwards we fell asleep in each other's arms.

The alarm clock woke us both. As I reached over to turn

it off, Steve reached for me.

"Whoa," I said. "Want to miss your plane?"

"What plane?"

Soon he was inside me again. He felt so good, like he really belonged there. After our morning quickie, we got up and showered together. As I walked him to his car, we exchanged phone numbers and promised to keep in touch.

I couldn't wait until the next month!

July

People come to Las Vegas from all over the world to see the spectacular Fireworks shows during the Fourth of July holiday. July also brings conventions of video dealers, office machine dealers, and the International Order of Elks. Families are back, pools are terrific, and the hotels are back to capacity again.

I had been visiting various casinos in order to learn more about craps. I'd been watching the tables and studying how people play to see if there was any pattern to consistent winning. In some of these excursions I would see Jack. He obviously had not stopped gambling like he had told me and it occurred to me that he might have an addiction.

Even though our relationship hadn't really developed into anything more than a casual friendship, he was my first real craps teacher. I decided to call Gamblers Anonymous at 1-800-GAMBLER and see what I could do to help. They sent me a number of brochures which I started to carry around with me, while waiting to see Jack again. I had a good idea about how to bring up the subject so he wouldn't be offended.

The next time I ran into him was at Caesars Palace, another one of my favorite casinos. Caesars is a "Grand" casino, meaning expensive, posh and elegant. They have a wonderful indoor mall, with an ever-changing sky on the ceiling and a group of large, animated talking figures in the center of the mall. That always draws a crowd and you should not miss it on your next trip to Vegas! They have great restaurants and most of the staff dresses in togas. My kind of place!

Anyway, when I spotted Jack he was playing craps, as usual. It looked as if he was about finished, judging by his small pile of chips.

"Hi," I said, "How about a banana daiquiri?"

He flushed and looked guilty, as though I had caught him doing something wrong.

"Oh. Tina. Hi! I was just, uh, playing here a few minutes. Stopped by to see a friend. Sure, a drink sounds nice. I'm done here anyway."

He scooped up his small pile of chips and we found a quiet bar, where we could talk. I ordered banana daiquiris for both of us.

"So, what's up?" I started.

"Tina, it's so good to see you again! I came up with a terrific craps system!"

I wondered how many systems he had come up with in the last few months.

"I play the five, six and eight and bet on the field. I have all the numbers covered. I can't lose!"

"Jack, what if a seven rolls? You lose all your bets."

"But that rarely happens! On a long roll I'll win hundreds and . . . "

"Jack, how's your wife? Your family?"

"Huh? Oh. They're OK."

"Listen, Jack, I was wondering if you can help me. One of my friends is a compulsive gambler. He gambles all the time and neglects his family and his job. I sent away for some information for him, and since you know so much about gambling, could you look it over for me and let me know what you think of it? I really want to help him, and maybe you can tell me if this information is worthwhile."

Silence. "Well . . . "

"I would *really* appreciate it, Jack." I took out my packet of pamphlets. "Could you look over this stuff and meet me here tomorrow, same time, same place, and tell me what you think? If everything is OK, then I can give it all to my friend."

No response.

"Look, it will only take a few minutes of your time. Please, Jack. You'll really be helping out my friend."

Silence. "Imnotacomplusivegambler," he blurted out.

"Oh Jack, of course you're not. It's for a friend."

I held out the pamphlets. He grabbed them and left. Didn't even finish his drink. Oh well, no use letting it go to waste. I watched him go and he didn't return to the craps tables, at least not there.

After he left, I wandered around the casino for a while, taking it all in, and noticed a sign advertising Caesars new OmniVision movie, about dangerous underwater creatures. I've always wanted to try scuba diving, but I should probably learn how to swim first. Still, I decided to see the movie.

The OmniVision Theater is a huge, 80' high curved theater. It is really spectacular! You lean back in your seat which is set at a very steep angle, then tilt your head back and movie is all around you. Unfortunately, I couldn't concentrate. My mind was going in all directions. I thought about Steve, and what might happen to our relationship if I were to tell him about my profession. If I did, would I ever see him again? We had spoken several times on the phone and I chickened out each time.

And, Jack. Had I done any good butting my nose into his business? Would I ever see Big Red again? And what happened to Yvonne? I had called her at home and left messages but they weren't returned.

When the movie ended I walked one very long block to the Mirage to talk to the dolphins. I always get cheered up by them, and this time was no exception. They're such wonderful creatures and they always look like they're smiling and having fun! I resolved to smile all the time, too, and felt better immediately. I was in good health, had some money saved up and I was still young. I just knew there was an exciting future in store for me.

I was in a terrific mood all afternoon long, and when I got home there was a message, finally, from Yvonne. She wanted to know if I could have dinner with her. I called back immediately and agreed. It seems she had been in New York for a special project, for a few weeks. She didn't elaborate and I didn't pry.

She told me to dress elegantly, so I picked a short, clingy black dress with fringe that moved with the motion of my body. I swept my hair up, catching it with a gold clip. A gold evening bag and matching shoes complemented the outfit. I'm glad I dressed well, because the dinner turned out to be very important! Finally, I was ready, and drove to the Imperial Palace to meet her.

The Imperial Palace has an oriental theme, but it is known for its excellent automobile museum on the top floor. I met Yvonne at an elegant looking restaurant there called Embers.

"Oh, Tina," she said, "you look wonderful! Sit down. I've ordered stuffed oysters as an appetizer for both of us. Hope that's OK."

Yvonne, as usual, looked stunning! She was wearing a yellow off-the-shoulder cocktail dress that emphasized her figure beautifully!

"Gee, this place looks expensive . . . "

"Oh, Tina, don't worry, my treat. I have a credit voucher here so this won't cost us anything. So, how are things with you?"

I wondered what she wanted. I told her about Steve and

Jack and Marv and a slew of other things. Yvonne doesn't play craps; in fact she doesn't gamble at all. There was more small talk, lots of catching up and then she finally got to the point.

"Tina, are you happy doing what you're doing?"

"Sometimes, sometimes not. I do wonder what I'll be doing in twenty years. I was thinking of taking singing lessons."

"Can I ask you a personal question?"

"Shoot."

"Do you have any money saved up?"

"Why?"

"Well, I have an idea how we can leave hooking forever. A friend of mine has a club he wants to get rid of, quick. It includes the liquor license and he'll let it go for a hundred grand. I have two other friends who are interested so if the four of us invest $25,000 each we can buy it, fix it up, and split the profits!"

I thought about it for a minute. I did have over $25,000 saved up. But, what would I do if the venture failed and I lost it? At this point, I was not convinced.

"Think about it." Yvonne said. "We would run it ourselves. It will be a quiet place, soft music, with artsy nude or topless dancers. No loud music, no disco. Class joint. Men have to wear ties. Maybe we could put on some high-class shows."

And what if it did succeed? I would be respectable. I would control my own destiny. I would make something of myself. It's another gamble, win or lose, like craps. I smiled, and thought of the dolphins playing. This would be just like more playing and, if it failed, I could always earn more money, somewhere, somehow, doing something. And, I would still have $15,000 left over to live on for a few months.

"I have a lot of contacts, and so do the other girls. I'm sure you must know some who might want to help, too."

I immediately thought of Big Red and his construction business, but I didn't know how to contact him.

"This will be a great club, and I know we can do it. Between the four of us, we certainly have the smarts, the talent and the contacts. Now the permits . . . "

"I'll do it," I said, a little surprised at myself.

She looked at me and smiled, then moved over and gave me a hug.

"*We'll* do it!" she said, and we both smiled.

The oysters came and they were delicious, the best I've ever eaten. The rest of the food was terrific too, but I was thinking constantly, even while Yvonne was talking. A new career, a new life. No more hooking.

After we left, I brought Yvonne home with me for a drink and showed her my craps table. And my bedroom.

"Mind if I get out of these clothes?" she asked.

"Here, let me help you, Mistress Pearl," I said as she chuckled.

I slipped off her dress and stared at her large brown breasts poking out of a lacy beige bra, which I also removed. Her matching beige panties followed. Her skin was like satin as she encircled me with her arms and we kissed. Then it was my turn and she had me stripped in a blink of an eye.

"Oh, Mistress Pearl," I whined. "I've never made love to a woman right after eating at Embers on a Friday in July in Las Vegas at 9:00 in the evening!"

She laughed hysterically!

We went to bed, kissing and caressing each other, and played for what seemed like hours.

When we were both finally satiated we started talking and talking and talking.

"What got you started in the profession?" she asked me.

"Gee. Centuries ago I moved from New York to L.A. to become a star. So did about a million other girls. I tried waitressing but it didn't pay much and I never had any money. One day I was so broke, I couldn't even afford to put gas in my car so I could get to the next audition. There was a guy at a gas station who kept flirting with me every time I went there, so I thought maybe he would give me some free gas. Well, he wanted something in exchange for the gas. I wasn't thrilled with the idea, but I really needed the money. It seems so silly now, but that's how it started. Once it happened, it seemed like a pretty easy way to make some money. Later I got a job as a stripper and got paid lots more than a tank of gas. That also made it easier to get paying dates. What about you?"

"Oh, I was born in Compton, near L.A. We never had any money. When I was 15, some of the other girls my age were already hooking. It was part of the community, I guess. Depending on the girl, the cash was either used to support the family, support their pimp or to pay for drugs. That wasn't for me, though. I looked at it as a way out. I saved up my money and left, as soon as I could. My mom didn't care one bit and I never knew my dad. I've never been back."

We were both silent for a minute. I looked in her eyes and we hugged and cried, holding each other.

"We'll make this club succeed, Tina, I know we will!"

"Yes, we will," I said, turning off the light. We fell asleep in each other's arms.

In the morning, we discussed the initial plans for the club. Yvonne would work on the legalities of the purchase and get the publicity machine in motion. Plus, she had to coordinate everything with the other girls. She left mid-morning, full of plans and enthusiasm!

Two days later I got a phone call and we made an appointment to meet the following day at the site of the club on Boulder Highway. The next day, full of excitement, I drove over and met my other two partners, Andrea and Barbara. Before long, a press photographer arrived for pictures and an interview.

The next day I was horrified! On page two of the daily paper the headline was "Hookers Form Club". And, I was in the picture! I don't know how I could have missed what the interviewer was getting at. The whole gist of the story was that the hookers were going legit. It just never occurred to me that a story like that would be news. What if Steve should see it! I called Yvonne and she thought it was cute, and would give us some free publicity. Steve couldn't have seen it. He just couldn't have.

Two weeks later he was supposed to be at the Trop. When the time came, I called and he wasn't there. I called the Excalibur, Luxor, and every other hotel I could think of. I called him numerous times at home and just got his machine.

He must have seen the paper.

I had lost him.

I was very depressed so I called Yvonne and she came right over and we talked.

"He's just a guy," she said. "You'll find others." Things like that.

She wanted to play around with me but I just wasn't in the mood. To cheer me up, she told me about the plans for the as yet unnamed club.

Yvonne was really the head honcho with the club. The rest of us were just along for the ride at this point. She was coordinating everything and all we had done was invest. So far, it was working out well.

"We really have a lot of interest in it, Tina. I think it's

going to be a big hit! Lots of people want to become involved, and I'm hoping we can open by Christmas!"

Her bubbly enthusiasm did make me feel better. Even if I never saw Steve again, I wanted to stop hooking. I decided to take singing lessons. Maybe buy some books on singing, if there were any. If I could learn craps, I could learn how to sing!

When Yvonne left, I was excited. I made a decision and called my service and canceled. No more hooking! I went to a local Bookstar and found two books on singing and I found a voice teacher in the Yellow Pages. Then I drove to the club site on Boulder Highway. Construction people were working already. The sign said Hamlish Construction. Things were really moving along.

The next day I met Yvonne, Andrea and Barbara at the Jockey Club. There were two lawyers there with a lot of papers to sign and be notarized. We all gave our checks to the lawyers in return for receipts and copies of the documents.

Afterwards I told Yvonne of my decision to stop hooking, and that I had canceled my service.

"I canceled too," she said. "Say, Tina, do you happen to know of an accountant who would work for us until the club opens?"

Yvonne knew that I had majored in accounting and had some accounting jobs in L.A. Why not, I thought.

"I'll try, Yvonne. I'll have to get some books and study, but I'll give it a go!"

"That's great! I'll be working full time on the club, so I'm sure we'll be seeing a lot of each other!" She winked at me. "Oh, I almost forgot. One of my friends has donated a computer and I want you to have it. Ever use one?"

"No. But I'll learn."

"Good. I'll bring it over later today. You can keep the

books on it."

She had some other business to do and left, promising that she would see me in two hours. I drove to a nearby computer superstore and bought the software program I would need the most - a computer Craps simulator!

By the time Yvonne arrived, I had finished reading the instruction manual for the game. We brought the computer in, and placed it on my kitchen table, next to the Craps table. She showed me how to turn it on, and load an accounting program called "Quicken". Then she brought in a box of books that told me how to use all of the programs.

She had to leave, unfortunately, and left me with the books. I called Steve to tell him I had a computer, but as usual, just left a message on his machine.

So, I loaded the craps program and was amazed at the technology available! It came complete with voices and moving characters. Still, I was restless. I needed to get out of the house and do something fun. So I decided, surprise, surprise, to leave the computer for the real thing.

I went back to the Trop, looking in vain for Steve, but he was nowhere to be found. This was his favorite casino, and every time I was in the neighborhood, I stopped in, thinking that perhaps he had made an unscheduled visit.

I elbowed my way into a busy table to watch the action. They still had their "Roll three elevens for $5000" promotion, but no one was betting on it.

The table was choppy and one of the things I noticed was that people weren't switching their bets at all. People either bet with or against the dice all the time. I decided to try something.

If the last point was made, I bet on the pass line and, at the same time, placed the six and eight for $12 each. If the point sevened out, I would switch to the don't-pass. Surprisingly, this worked pretty well, and at the end of a half hour, I was ahead by $220!

Then, a man who reminded me of Big Red, came up to the table and looked like he would own it. He played for a while and won. When he became the shooter, he bet $1 on the eleven, so I did the same. He had *confidence*. I had *confidence*. We were going to win! One eleven rolled and everyone cheered! The next roll was another eleven. Everyone was quiet. I closed my eyes and opened them to the sound of everyone yelling. We had both won $5000!

The pit boss rushed over and congratulated us! A casino host led us to an office where we signed some papers and received a check, right there on the spot. Then, they took our pictures. For the second time, my picture was in the paper but this time my occupation was listed as "Night Club Owner".

The man who won with me was an accountant, so we had something in common. We went for drinks and he said he was a CMA, a Certified Management Accountant. He told me about the certification process and right then and there, I decided to forego my voice lessons and become a CMA. I was never a good singer anyway and wanted to do my best to help the club.

He explained the difference between a CPA, a Certified Public Accountant, and a CMA. A CPA does mostly company audits and reports to external organizations while a CMA reports to internal organizations and runs the company financially. He said I could be a CMA in less than two years, if I worked hard.

So, now my goal was studying computers and accounting in my *spare* time, as well as being in temporary charge of the financial dealings of "The Club", which was our working name. I was on my way! No more hooking. Even if The Club failed, I would have a real profession. But The Club wouldn't fail. It couldn't.

Who needed Steve anyway?

August

August is the month for Surplus Merchandise dealers. It is also the month that most people take vacations, so Las Vegas is full.

August eventually turned out to be a great month for me! It started out at the Excalibur Hotel. Yvonne, Andrea, Barbara and I had a meeting there to sort out some of the issues relating to The Club. First of all, we decided to name it Oui Gals for now. We also decided not to accept outside investments. As Yvonne had been telling us, a lot of the movers and shakers in town and high rollers from out of town had heard of our venture and wanted a piece of the action. We were getting a lot of calls from all the publicity. It would have given us a little cushion in the financial department, but we were determined not to give up any ownership. Oui Gals would be owned jointly and solely by the four of us. Everything was proceeding smoothly, and the front facade was nearly finished. Oui Gals is pretty far from the strip, and it was requiring a great deal of work from all of us, much more than we had expected.

After the meeting, I went down to the craps tables, just to look around. I found a busy, hot table where the numbers just kept rolling. I would wait for a seven to roll, and bet $30 on the six and eight Then, when either of them hit, I would take both bets down. This worked great, and after an hour of playing, I was ahead almost $300! Then I lost twice in a row so I quit and headed across the street to the Trop, just in case you-know-who was there.

I strolled across the overhead walkway between the Excalibur and the Tropicana, taking it easy and enjoying the scenery. It was kind of nice to look down on the cars rushing to their hotels. I was carrying my leather briefcase full of papers, mostly about Oui Gals. I was thinking about, believe it or not, the Oui Gals bathrooms, and not thinking about my briefcase at all. It was expensive leather, a present from one of my former clients.

Suddenly a rough looking man rushed me from behind, grabbed my briefcase, and started to run off! I was so shocked I didn't move! I screamed!

"Help! That man just stole my briefcase!"

Finally I woke up and started running after him, yelling, but he was almost at the down escalator! All of a sudden a man who was coming up the escalator, saw what was happening and tackled the robber! They struggled for a few seconds and suddenly the robber broke away, leaving the briefcase behind. Some other people saw what was going on and stopped him! I finally caught up to the knot of people, and got the shock of my life when I took a look at my rescuer. It was Steve!

The police showed up in minutes. The Las Vegas P.D. are the best in the world! Steve and I hugged and kissed. His arms felt so good around me. We looked into each other's eyes all the way down the escalator. We walked into the Trop, hand in hand, and headed for the bar overlooking the pool where we had first met.

"I tried to find you," I said. "I called the Trop so many times but they couldn't help. I called you in San Diego and left dozens of messages on your machine, but you never called back. I thought that you weren't interested in me because of, well, my profession, my former profession now . . . "

"I saw the newspaper article. You should have told me the

truth."

"I wanted to, believe me, but I thought you wouldn't want to see me anymore."

"I would have liked it more if you were honest with me. The truth is very important, and even though I liked you a lot, I did not want a relationship that began with a lie. I was about ready to look for you again, though. I discovered that I really missed you."

"So, does it make any difference that I used to be a . . . prostitute?"

"No. In fact, it's kind of exciting! But promise me you'll never lie to me again!"

"Oh, Steve, I promise!"

We hugged again.

"So, how is your new club coming along? When is it opening?"

"We're hoping for Christmas. I'll send you an engraved invitation. What were you doing on the escalator anyway?"

"Actually, I was on my way over to the Excalibur for dinner. I was in the mood for a buffet, and I like the one there better than the one at MGM or the Trop."

"I was just coming back from a meeting at the Excalibur. I thought I'd mosey around the craps tables here," I said, trying to be overly honest with him. Maybe Steve was "The One" and I didn't want to lie to him ever again.

"I could go for some dinner, too and I've never eaten at the Excalibur. Uh, mind if I join you?"

"That would be great," he said smiling.

I love his smile. We turned around and walked back outside again, toward the escalators, heading for the hotel.

The Excalibur looks like a huge castle and has a King Arthur theme. It's on three levels, with the casino in the middle. Downstairs they have a show called King Arthur's

Tournament and a simulation ride. On the third level are all of the restaurants. At night, right outside on the corner, a dragon battles with Merlin the Magician in a light show.

We went to the buffet, but it was very crowded. Steve told me that there is usually a long line for "credit card payments only" but the "cash only" line is short. This time, both lines were long.

"Hey," said Steve. "Have you ever seen the Show? The Jousting Tournament?"

"Nope, what's it like?"

"Well, it's a great show. It's like you're back in the middle ages, with knights on horseback, magic, real jousting, a horse show and lots more. Dinner is included, but you have to eat it with your hands. It's really a lot of fun. You can wave your drumstick and cheer for your favorite knight! Want to go there?"

"Sure, sounds . . . interesting," I said unconvinced. Jousting? Knights?

We went all the way downstairs, bought tickets, and then had two hours to wait for the show. So, naturally, we went back up to the casino to the craps tables.

We settled in at the table where I had been playing earlier, but it had an entirely new crowd. The table must have cooled down.

Steve started playing while I watched for a while. He was betting the pass line, and if a six or eight was the point, he would place double odds, a five or nine, single odds, a four or ten, no odds. After two points in a row sevened out, he switched to the don't side, betting don't pass, with three don't come bets. It was a pretty simple and safe system, and after a while I joined him, betting the same way. After almost two hours of playing, he was ahead $80 and I was ahead $40. We asked if we could get comped to the Show, which we already had tickets for, but the pit boss said we didn't play enough. He said he'd give us two buffet tickets, though, which we took and saved. It never hurts to ask for comps, even if you don't need them right then.

The auditorium downstairs looked like a circus tent, and everyone sat next to each other on benches. The food, when it came, was a small chicken, a potato, and some broccoli. We had to eat this with our hands, no utensils. At first I didn't like it but before long everyone was talking to everyone else, trading food, and rooting for "our" knight.

We got in the spirit of things by feeding each other with our fingers and then licking them off. Our knight was the Green knight, since we were sitting in the Green section. Soon the battle had begun, and I was really getting into it! There were swords clanging, jousts being smashed, people yelling and screaming, great fun, and the food tasted better as we went along. It was one of the most fun shows ever, even the little kids were cheering and yelling! There was a small magic show in the middle and, at the end, a Princess was chosen from the audience by the winning knight!

The Jousting finished for the night and as the lights came back on, we worked our way out, through the crowd.

"Are you staying at the Trop?" I asked.

"Yes," said Steve solemnly.

"Want to come back to my place for a drink?"

"Yes," said Steve with a big smile.

We walked back across the overpass to the Trop and got both of our cars. His was a rental, a Suzuki Sidekick of all things, and he followed me home.

I made us both Kahlua and Coke and we sat down on the couch, lost in each other's eyes. We talked a little, mostly about honesty and friendship.

I went into the kitchen to make more drinks and Steve

came up behind me and put his arms around me. I turned around and he kissed me, hard. I held him tight and thought, oh, Steve, don't leave me again. When I looked up at him and saw those beautiful green eyes of his looking into mine, I took his hand and led him to the bedroom.

I soon found out that the jousting was not quite over for the knight.

September

September is a big month for conventions. The National Office Products Association, the American Baker Association, and the Men's Apparel Guild, all meet in September, bringing over 100,000 people to Las Vegas.

I spent most of my time working on Oui Gals, my computer and studying my accounting books. I was on the phone with Steve constantly, asking his advice on such subjects as "File Not Found", "General Protection Fault", and "Fatal Error". Computers are such fun.

On the third weekend, Steve finally arrived for his monthly mini-vacation. He was going to stay at the Trop, as usual. I met him at the airport Saturday morning and took him to my condo. I hadn't been with anyone since his last visit and we both were impatient. As soon as we opened the door we were hugging and kissing and leaving a trail of clothes into the bedroom.

Afterwards, we lay naked, our bodies entwined and talked. He asked me about my years as a hooker, my aspirations, and my studies. We talked for hours and hours, totally open with each other. It was a wonderful feeling, being with someone with whom I could share my soul, and my body as well. We talked and snoozed the day away, made love when we awakened, talked some more and then fell asleep again.

We finally woke up for good around 6:00 pm and Steve told me he had a new system he wanted to try. He wanted to go to Binions to do it, because they have no table limits there. Steve told me he had learned how to play craps at Binions and thought the dealers were a little more lenient than at other places. He also said he wanted to bet on the eleven, which paid 15 to one. The true odds of the eleven or three are 18 to one, which means that they should hit once every 18 rolls.

His idea was to bet just on the eleven or Yo, but only after there were seven consecutive rolls with no Yo. Then he would increase his bet by a progressive system each time. He would add the current bet to the bet number to get the next bet. For example, the first betting progression would be bet #1=$1, #2=$2, #3=$4, #4=$7, #5=$11, #6=$16, and so on. On the tenth bet, which was really the 17th roll after he started, he would be betting $45 on the Yo. The total amount he would have bet was $173 so far and if the Yo rolled on the tenth roll, he would win 45 x 15, or $675. Subtract $173 from $675 and he would have a $502 profit!

He showed me how he worked this all out on my computer craps game at home. The money won would keep increasing until the 29th roll, where he would be betting $408 on the Yo. The total played so far would be $4,101 and if the Yo hit on that 29th roll, he would win $6,120, for a profit of $2,019!

However, from the 30th roll on, the winnings would decrease, until the 44th roll, where he would lose $41. On this 44th roll, he would be betting $948 and winning $14,220, but his total in play would be $14,261. So, he figured that if we ever made it to the 44th roll, we'd have to add an extra $5 to each bet to make a profit.

Steve brought $20,000 with him to try this scheme. I was very skeptical of the large bankroll he needed, but Steve said he just couldn't lose. We drove down to Binions and walked to the crap tables. I looked around for Jack but he was nowhere to be found.

We found a medium active table with six players and we

stood across from the stick man. We just watched for a while and I counted the rolls. Six rolls with no eleven. It was time to bet. On the come out roll Steve bet $1 on the Yo. We made sure there were no table limits, and told the dealer we might be making some big bets. He said it was fine with him. The point was nine, which eventually was made. Still no eleven. Steve was on bet #8, $29. In five more rolls, bet #13, the eleven rolled! Steve had $79 on the Yo, won $1185, had total bets of $373, so he made a $812 profit!

We tried it again. Waited seven rolls, and bet $1 on the Yo. This time it rolled on the fourth roll, with only $7 bet, giving us a profit of $89. Then we changed tables, just for luck, Steve said.

We made sure there were no table limits again and told the pit boss we might be making bets of $1000 or more. He just smiled and welcomed us. Everyone is so nice at Binions. We waited seven more rolls and began betting on the Yo again. This time we waited and waited for the elusive eleven. Steve was betting $302 (his 25th bet) and had already played $2633. Finally, on the 32nd roll, the eleven came up. He had $498 bet, won $7470, played $5503, so he made $1967!

I was getting really nervous with all these big bets, but Steve was way ahead and wanted to win once more. He waited another seven rolls and bet the Yo. This time, it took until the 21st roll, where he had a $212 bet, had spent $1565, and, won $3180. He had $1615 in profit.

Now, we were both getting nervous and Steve was tired. We had been playing for three hours. He looked at me and agreed immediately when I suggested we stop. We asked the pit boss for two gourmet dinners, which he gladly gave us. Then, we cashed out and made out way over to the cashier's cage. It turned out that we had won $4483! Not bad for three hours of work!

We took the elevator up to the restaurant, called Binions Skyroom, a wonderful place with a terrific view of all of Las Vegas!

While we were waiting for our table, we stared down at the neon lights of downtown, each lost in thought. In a few minutes our table was ready. We ordered and started talking.

"You know," said Steve, "we could have won more money if we were betting on both the three and the eleven. It would be harder to keep track of, but we would win more. Maybe you could bet on the three and I'll stick to the eleven!"

"But weren't you nervous with so much money being bet? And what if the eleven didn't roll until the 80th roll? You would really get behind."

"Sometimes it's good to get a little behind," Steve snickered. "But, no, we couldn't lose money. The break-even point was 44 rolls for the Yo. Past that we would have to increase our bets by five dollars. But remember, we started betting on the eighth roll, so it was really 52 rolls. I would bet that an eleven would roll once in 52 rolls. It's a pretty safe bet."

The food was good, but the company was better.

"And," he continued, "I have credit at Binions. If I spent over $20,000 I would just have to keep betting until an eleven came up. Eventually, it would. Let's talk about something else. I need to get my mind off gambling. So, what's happening with the club? I know you went to a meeting yesterday. How's it going?"

"Oh, its going great! The opening is set for New Years Eve! We've decided to open it during the daytime for lunch with reasonable prices to get people in, and then sell stuff at the tables. The gals will walk around modeling lingerie which we'll sell, along with sexy toys and some men's wear. I think it'll go over big!"

"Oh, eh, are any of the girls in, uh, your former profession?"

"Well, yes, but most of us don't want to hook any more. The girls will be honest with the patrons and tell them where they can find a prostitute if they want one. Most men are very reasonable when they know they have to pay for sex. If the girls flirt with the men, they'll buy more stuff, maybe for the girls themselves, as tips. We're now working on getting some Japanese groups there for a "free" lunch on Valentine's Day. I think it'll go over very well!"

"Wow, sounds like you're all doing a lot of work on this! And no problem with the liquor license?"

"None at all. The gals have *lots* of contacts. And at lunchtime we'll have drink specials, maybe for a dollar. If people drink more they'll buy more. All of the items will sell for over $50, so the more they drink the better!"

"And they'll be no gambling?"

"No, not even slots. This will be a classy place. We'll even have Oui Gals skimpy T-shirts, mugs, and other souvenir items available on the way out. If no one buys the high ticket items, maybe we can sell them a few mugs or pens. Once someone gets in the door, they'll be so pampered and fussed over, they'll want to buy something!"

"That's great! Sounds like you've got a real winner there. By the way, I'll be back here for another four days next month . . . have any plans?"

"Eh, no, why?"

"Maybe we can spend the four days together, either at the Trop or your place. It'll be fun to spend all four days together, just to see how things work out."

Hmm, what did he mean by that? Is he thinking of some kind of permanent relationship?

"Sure, why not, my place is fine," I said with stars in my

eyes.

We finished the meal, looked down on our town and left. Back at my condo we made wonderful, glorious love. Afterwards he held me tight and looked into my eyes.

"I love you, Tina."

"I love you, too, Steve."

He didn't go back to the Trop that night. As we snuggled, I dreamed of our future, Oui Gals and, of course, craps.

The next day we worked out our three/Yo plan. Steve would bet on the eleven and I would bet on the three. We would both wait for seven rolls without the three or eleven before we started betting.

We went back to Binions to try it out. Walking across the casino, I literally bumped into Jack.

"Tina!" He exclaimed, "Look . . . I, uh, just wanted to thank you, thank you very much for that information . . . " He kissed me on the cheek and was gone.

"Who was that?" Steve asked, staring at me.

"Oh, let's sit down, I'll tell you all about it." We found a lounge and I told him all I could about Jack. Everything, nothing held back. I would never lie to Steve again.

"Tina, I think that's great," he said. "Maybe you really helped him. And thanks for being so honest."

"I love you, Steve. I'll never lie to you again. Come on, now, let's go play craps!"

We bought in for $1000 each and counted. A three rolled right away so I had to start my count over and bet independently of Steve. I also had to concentrate on what I was doing, not on what he was doing, so I tried to ignore his bets altogether. Soon there were seven rolls with no three so I bet $1, then $2, $4, etc. The three finally hit on bet #8, I had $29 bet, spent $92, and won $435, giving me a $343 profit.

I started betting on a new series, but a three never rolled.

Twenty rolls went by, then thirty. I was betting over $500 each time and getting nervous. I thought about Steve - "It's a sure thing!" and Big Red - "Have confidence!". I smiled. I was going to beat this game. I am invincible! The 40th roll passed. So what, I was betting almost $900 on one number. So what, it's only money. Easy money. I smiled and smiled. I was going to win. Finally, the three rolled on the 43rd roll! I had bet $905 on that roll, and had won $13,575, but had spent $13,313, giving me a profit of *only* $262. I could hardly breathe!

I stopped playing, but Steve was still at it. I watched him for a while, until he won, and pulled him away.

"Let's go! I have a hunch we should stop now." As everyone knows in craps, you should always play your hunches, so he quit too. We had made over $2000 in less than two hours!

We cashed out, got some more comps, and started to drive back to my place. I was silent for a minute.

"Steve, even though this seemed to be a good system, it was nerve wracking, and I don't want to do it anymore. It wasn't fun, and I had to concentrate too hard on everything and make sure my count was right. If I forgot to place a bet and a three came up I would lose everything. You want me to be honest, and I am. I like to have fun playing craps and this was torture. You can play this way if you want, but I won't do it anymore."

"Tina, I don't want to play this way any more either, but for a completely different reason."

"Oh, and what is that, may I ask?"

"I have a new system in development at home. Next month I'll show it to you. To be a good craps player, you can't depend on just one system. You need to know everything about the game, and be able to play in any way the game warrants. I just wanted to try out this system, to see if it would work, and it did."

What a relief! Steve wasn't mad at me. And, we were driving back to my condo, not the Trop. I had a hunch that this relationship might work out after all. As everyone knows, you should always play your hunches!

October

October is the month that hosts the Las Vegas Invitational Golf Tournament and the American Mining Congress. It was also the month that the Oui Gals front sign was installed. The booths and stage were ready and Yvonne was already making plans to have some lounge acts in January. Everything was almost ready, and if we rushed, we could probably open for Christmas, but all the advertising said New Years, so that was that.

I received a call from Andrea, inviting us to see her in a show at Harrahs, called "Spellbound". I picked up Steve at the airport, as usual, but this time he would be staying at my condo, not at a hotel. It was going to be a new and hopefully exciting experience for both of us. He was in a great mood, having just sold a book on CD ROM technology. My computer had a CD ROM but I really didn't care how it worked, just that it did. We threw his bags in the trunk and were off, to *our* home.

"So, what is this great new system you have?" I asked. "I hope it doesn't involve counting the threes and elevens."

"Well, actually you count the twos and twelves . . . no, no, I'm kidding, don't worry, it's pretty simple. Pretty much how we've been playing all along. You bet mostly from the don't side. Start with $40 don't pass and lay the four and ten for $40 each for insurance and take them down after the point is established. Pretty simple so far, huh. Then we just bet the inside numbers *and* bet don't come at the same time. If the don't come lands on any inside number, we'll win and take it down. If the seven rolls, we win on the don't pass. If the point hits, we hopefully will have won enough from the inside bets to offset the don't pass bet."

It did sound pretty simple and it sounded like an easy system to master. I wondered why no one had thought of it before. "We can try it at, uh, home, with my baby craps table."

"Well, I was thinking of something else we could do first, that is, if you don't mind." He winked at me lasciviously.

When we arrived at my condo we headed straight for the bedroom. I started to take off my clothes, but Steve stopped me.

"I want to do this. You just relax."

He unbuttoned my blouse and took it off, lightly touching my bra. Then he removed my shoes and skirt. He started caressing my body and I reached out for him, but he stopped me again.

"Relax. Just let me do everything."

He sat me down on the bed and removed my stockings, caressing my legs as he did so. I was getting really excited. I wanted him now! He removed my panties slowly and, finally, my bra. I sat naked before him, looking up at him. He started removing his clothes slowly, until he too was naked and definitely ready.

He knelt down in front of me and pushed his head in my lap, gently licking me. Just as I was ready to come, he stood up quickly, picked me up in his arms, as rolled me on the bed with him on top. He grabbed my hands and put them above my head and entered me. It felt so good to have him in me again. "I missed you so much," I said to him. He kissed me, and started thrusting, until he brought me to the most loving orgasm I've ever had. Love really does make a difference. Then he started again, until we both had our climaxes once more.

We lay in each other's arms, sharing a contented afterglow, when he rolled over and said those three magic words I love to hear . . . "Let's Play Craps!" I hit him with my pillow and we started wrestling like little kids. What can I say, I love the game, but I love Steve more. We took a shower together then headed for Harrah's.

It was much too early for Andrea's show, so we ambled over to the craps tables. We bought in for $500 each and we both played Steve's system. I bet $40 no-four, $40 no-ten, and $40 don't pass. Fortunately, the point was five, so I took the no-four and no-ten down, and placed the six, eight and nine, and also made a $10 don't come bet. The six hit so I took it down and put another don't come bet up. Then the nine. Another don't come. Then a seven rolled. I had won $40 on my don't pass, $14 each on the six and nine, and $20 on the don't comes. I lost $12 on the eight and one $10 don't come bet. Not a bad start.

I tried the same way again, $40 no-four, $40 no-ten, and $40 don't pass. A seven. I won $40 but lost $40. Same bet again. This time a three rolled, I won $40. The next roll was six, the point. I still did the same thing, I took down the no-four and no-ten, bet don't come, and placed the five, eight and nine. The four, ten, and nine rolled, so I had three don't come bets up. Then the eight rolled, and then, the six. I had won $28 but lost $40. Then, there was a seven on the next come out, so I won an additional $30 on the don't comes and $40 on the new don't four and ten!

This seemed to be a pretty easy system, and it was fun to play. We didn't win as much as we did last month, counting the threes and elevens, but it was much less stressful, and much more fun!

I looked over at Steve and he seemed to be doing well too. This is what craps should be, having fun, and winning a little bit of money and a lot of comps.

I bet the same way again, and this time the point was nine. I had every number hit before the shooter sevened out! I was now ahead almost $100. I gave Steve a hug. This was great!

The two hours passed quickly, and it was time for the show. We asked for and received two free dinner tickets, which we saved, and went to the showroom, where we had two reserved seats waiting for us.

Spellbound was a terrific combination variety and magic show! We both thought that Andrea was the best of all the dancers. The magic was superb, as were the sets and costumes. We couldn't wait to see Andrea backstage.

We went back and were directed to a dressing room. Andrea was still topless and looked absolutely gorgeous.

"Tina! And this must be Steve," Andrea gushed. "I've heard quite a lot about you."

If I didn't know better, I could swear that Steve was staring at her breasts.

"Great to meet you, Andrea," Steve said. "You're the first one of Tina's partners I've had the pleasure to meet. I must say, you look a lot better in person than you did in that newspaper article."

"Oh, thanks, Steve. Tina's told us so much about you. Did you like the show?"

"It was great," we both chimed in. "And," I continued, "you were by far the best dancer there!" She blushed. Andrea's so cute. She still hadn't put her top on. I found myself getting strangely jealous. I did not want a threesome with her and Steve. I wanted him all to myself.

"Look," I said, "why don't you join us for dinner? We'll wait outside while you get dressed."

"Oh, you can stay here," she said. "I'm not exactly shy." Hmm. Steve *was* staring at her breasts and she didn't seem to mind at all.

After a few minutes of this I began to feel really uncomfortable so I told Steve I wanted to speak to him outside.

"We'll be right back," I yelled to Andrea.

"OK, what's up?" he said, smiling. As if he didn't know.

"Look, I promised to be honest, right? Well, I was feeling uncomfortable in there . . . you staring at Andrea's breasts like that. I'm sorry. I guess I shouldn't feel this way. Anyway I feel better now. Let's go back in."

"See, the truth really does work. Look, I'm not interested in sleeping with Andrea. But she *is* beautiful, and since I'm not dead, the sight of a woman's breasts is exciting to me. Yours especially. You shouldn't be jealous, I'm not in love with Andrea, I'm in love with you!"

"Oh, Steve. I love you too. And, I promise, I won't let it bother me anymore. You're bound to see lots of breasts . . ."

"I hope so," he smirked.

" . . . and I really am secure with you. But if I ever do get jealous, I'll let you know, deal?"

"O.K. Now, let's go back inside. Maybe Andrea's not finished dressing yet."

She was finished, and had changed into a simple, light green blouse and jeans. With no makeup on, and her hair let down, she looked like a different person, but all those curves were still there, hidden away.

Andrea's real name was, believe it or not, Andrea. It was the only name she used. Over dinner she told us that she was born in Northern Michigan and hated the cold and snow. After graduating from high school, she took the first chance she could to escape - she sold magazine subscriptions door-to-door with a "boiler-room" type team. She worked her way west to Las Vegas twenty years ago and here she stayed. She looked my age and we were both shocked when she told us she was 38!

"How do you stay so young looking?" I gasped.

"Well," she said, "I really like sex. Love it. I really think that a lot of sex makes you look younger, makes you smile more often and helps you live longer. My parents didn't treat me right — that's a long story — and I really crave the closeness of sex, but I don't want to settle down and have kids. I had my tubes tied and I want to stay young, single, free, and happy forever!"

"That's a terrific philosophy," Steve said, "but how do you fit into Oui Gals? Won't that settle you down somewhat?"

"Nope. I'm still doing my topless dancing. I love the way men look at me. And if a man really wants me, well . . . "

Steve was shocked, but I wasn't. Andrea is a wild one. The decision we all made to quit hooking was a verbal one, not a written contract.

"If we make a lot of money," Andrea continued, "maybe I'll quit then, but I'll never settle down, never. I'll go around the world, see everything I can. There's so much excitement in this world, I want to have it all!"

"Well, what will you do in ten years?" I asked.

"Oh, Tina, I'll find something. That's what's so exciting about life. Nothing is certain. Everything changes. The uncertainty is what I live for. What will I be doing in ten years? I can't wait to find out!"

Well, I had to admit she certainly had a positive attitude about things, which is surprising for a prostitute. And what surprised me even more, is that she asked us to teach her how to play craps. Steve signaled that I should tell her so I did.

I told her about the come out roll and the point, the seven before and after the come out, and the relationship of all the numbers on the dice to one another. She seemed to be taking it all in.

"I *am* following all this," she said. "I was always good at math. It seems like a much simpler game than I thought. If a seven hasn't rolled in a long time, you bet against the numbers, and if the seven has just rolled, you bet for the numbers, right?"

Steve and I looked at each other. She had just expressed a good basic system in one short sentence.

"Come on," she said, "I want to play!"

We went to the craps tables. Before we started to bet, we got a temporary comp card for Andrea and explained how comps worked. Then we all bought in for $300 each. Andrea's virginal system worked well. If a seven rolled, she bet on the six and eight, and took both bets down if either won. After five rolls with no seven, she started betting don't come. In less than an hour, she had won over $200!

"This is great!" she said. Everyone, as usual, was very friendly and helpful, especially the dealers. Steve and I were getting tired and said so. Andrea wanted to stay, so we left her there, in good hands.

We drove home, made wild passionate love, and fell asleep. The next morning, we got a call from Andrea.

"Hey, guys, I won fifteen hundred dollars!" she screamed in my ears. "I love this game! Where can I learn more about it?"

Andrea was, if you'll pardon the expression, hooked.

November

The beginning of November in Las Vegas means COMDEX, an electronics and computer convention that usually draws 200,000 people. The hotels for this week are filled way in advance and the room prices are double or triple the usual rate. Seems that COMDEX attendees are not gamblers and the hotels have to make a profit some way. There are special ads throughout the city advertising strange things like EXPAND YOUR MEMORY and DON'T GAMBLE WITH NO-NAME CHIPS. With my constantly increasing computer knowledge, even I was beginning to understand them.

Prostitution, of course, is very popular this week, about the only time all year that demand exceeds supply. I had numerous inquiries, through my former service, as to my availability. I could have made a lot this week, let me tell you.

I spent my time working at Oui Gals as much as I could, waiting for Thanksgiving week, when Steve would return. I also read about craps, every book I could find, and studied my financial and database programs, which I was using for the finances of Oui Gals. As with everything else, it took some getting used to, but I wanted to be an expert. The night classes I was taking in accounting really helped. I was going to make the financial wheels of Oui Gals spin quickly and profitably, at least until someone else took over.

I also had a complicated plan in mind to play craps. I was thinking about the threes and elevens we were playing with a few months ago. It didn't seem so stressful now, and I was ready to give it another try.

When Thanksgiving finally arrived, I met Steve at the airport. We played around for awhile in my condo, and then I suggested we go to the Stardust for lunch since I still had a comp there, plus lots of leftover match play coupons for craps. I had collected them previously at the end of their excellent show, "Enter The Night". Their coffee shop, called Toucan Harry's, is the best coffee shop in the world, with lots of exotic Chinese dishes, reasonable prices and, best of all, it was free and we didn't have to wait in line. There is *always* a line for Toucan Harry's.

Afterwards we went to play craps, of course. My plan was to wait for a 7 to roll and then bet on the inside numbers, the 5, 6, 8, and 9. When I won any two bets, I took everything down. I would also keep track of how many rolls between the 2, 3, 11 and 12, and bet on them.

If twenty rolls went by with no 3 or 11, I would bet $1, increasing by $1 each bet. Then, every twenty rolls I would increase the bet by $1. The same with the two and twelve, only I would start betting after 40 rolls instead of twenty.

I kept track of things by using my chip rack. I just knew that rack could be used for something other than for holding chips. I had my regular chips in the front rack and my counting chips in the rear. They were in four piles representing, in order, 2, 3, 11 and 12. With each roll of the dice I increased each pile by one chip. If one of the four numbers rolled, I reduced the pile to zero. When five $1 chips accumulated I replaced them with a $5 one, and when four $5 chips were piled up, I began betting on the 3 or 11. When eight $5 chips were piled up, I began betting on the 2 or 12.

This was considerably less complicated than Steve's formula from before. Let's say I am betting on the 3, which doesn't roll until the 30th roll. I started betting $1 on the 20th roll, and increased my bet by $1 on every roll. So, on the 30th roll, I have invested $55 so far in total, and have $10 bet on the 3. If it hits, I get a payoff of $150 (10 x 15), leaving me a profit of $95 (150-55).

This might not sound like much, but in the four hours we played, I won over $1100, most of which came from these bets. Steve was surprised by my system, and seemed glad I had overcome my objections from a few months ago.

He came up with another very basic system. If the last point sevened out, he would bet $44 inside. If the last point was made, he would bet three don't come bets. He did pretty well, and was ahead by just over $500 using this simple system.

One of the helpful dealers pointed out to me that I could bet the numbers 2, 3, 11 and 12 as one bet, called a "horn" bet. But, this could only be done in multiples of four, so my progression would be 4, 8, 12, 16, etc. I knew about the bet but it required too much money and too little pay off.

We finally "colored out", and asked for and got two more meal comps and two more shows. Since we had already eaten, and didn't feel like seeing the show again, we went home and made do with my one bed. Steve is a wonderful lover and always goes out of his way to please me. Sex is so much better with someone you love.

The next day we went exploring. Steve wanted to see the Stratosphere, and we stood in line until it was our turn to ride to the top. What a wonderful view of Las Vegas! It was so clear you could see forever. We decided not go on the roller coaster and took the elevator downstairs to the casino and added yet another comp card to our ever expanding collection.

It was still a nice day out so we walked a few blocks to the Sahara, and right inside the entrance we stumbled across the only craps slot machine either of us had ever seen. It only had a 25-cent minimum so we played a few rounds, but the rules were different and we ended up losing a whole $5. It was fun though. The Sahara has an African motif and was large and sprawling. We applied for comp cards there, but didn't play.

The Sahara is right next to Wet and Wild, a water park, which was closed for the winter. Then, being in a walking mood, we strolled down to Circus Circus, which was crowded as ever. It is the premier children's casino, with free circus acts and circus midway games especially for children. They also have Grand Slam Canyon, which is an enclosed amusement park featuring many rides for children.

We were getting kind of tired and hungry at this point so we took a taxi back to the car and checked our assorted comp tickets for food. I always try to get them without dates, but even if they are dated, I usually can get them exchanged at the pit. We finally decided on Treasure Island.

When we arrived, it wasn't crowded, probably due to the fact that the pirate battles hadn't started yet. While we were eating, Steve had a sudden burst of inspiration.

"I just thought of yet another system!" He exclaimed, "We just wait until a seven rolls and bet inside. Then we take everything down after one hit!"

"Huh?" I said, with a mouthful of cashew chicken.

"Are you finished eating? I want to try this!" he said.

Well I wasn't quite finished but I wanted to try it too. It looked interesting and simple. So we left a tip - we always tip big on comps - and walked out to the craps tables. We found one with a lot of chips on the table, some working come bets, and excited players. We were in the middle of a medium sized run. We gave the stick man our comp cards and bought in for $500 each, but didn't place any bets yet. When the shooter finally sevened out, the table applauded. Must have been a good run. Too bad we weren't in it from the beginning!

The next shooter continued, no come out seven, the point was a nine. Steve decided to bet $25 on three successive don't come bets which turned out to be the 5, 6 and 8. The next roll was a seven. He won $75 in five minutes! It was probably a strain to keep quiet, but he did. Don't bettors are not supposed to cheer and get rowdy, because everyone else loses money on the roll.

Since a seven had just rolled, we both bet $44 inside and watched the five and six hit. Steve took all his bets down after the five hit, but I pressed mine. I had a feeling. Another six, a nine, ten, two, five, another eight. I was way ahead, but I had another feeling, so I took my bets down. Another six rolled, drat, but then a seven.

Whenever I get a feeling I take my bets down. If I were positive a seven would roll, I would lay all the numbers, but my feelings aren't correct all the time. We were both ahead and decided to keep on playing.

A seven rolled, with a six point. We both bet $44 inside again. The five and nine rolled. Steve removed his bets after the five, I left them up. A seven, ugh. Steve smiled.

He said, "I'd rather make $14 on each point than take a chance on winning more."

"Yeah, but I'm still ahead. Can't win all the time. So now what? We had a very short run, are you still betting inside?"

"Let's wait this one out," he said, "No law says we have to bet every point."

The next point was an eight, and I was tempted to bet on it, but the very next roll was a seven. The table was "turning". Steve bet $10 don't pass. The next point was a five and Steve bet two don't come bets, on the six and ten. A two and four then rolled, so Steve had don't bets now on the five, six, four and ten. Thankfully, a seven rolled.

We agreed to stop, and asked for and received two more

comped buffets, for just under one hour of play. I love it when the casinos reward us for winning money!

We decided to take a break from craps and go for another walk. We walked the one long block to Caesars Palace, and went into the shops. We had both been there before, but I never tire of the glamour and excitement inside! We stopped at the Rotunda, waiting for the statues to reanimate, and then I saw someone I knew.

"Barbara!" I exclaimed, as we hugged each other. "Steve, this is the second of my partners. Barbara, this is Steve!"

"Great to meet you!" he said enthusiastically.

Barbara, fortunately, was dressed normally, a blue blouse with no cleavage, and jeans. She was 5'6" or so, curly black hair, and smiled so big you just had to hug her!

We watched the giant statues talk and move. It was a great, free show.

"Let's go for a drink," I said. We strolled over to Planet Hollywood, one of my favorite places. After we settled down, Steve asked her about her connection to Oui Gals.

"I'm the manager," Barbara said. "Right now I'm in charge of the contracts and seeing that everything gets done in time. Later, I'll manage the day-to-day aspects of the club, scheduling, advertising, souvenirs, food and drink. I managed a restaurant back in Brooklyn."

"You don't sound like a New Yawwker," Steve said, trying to imitate one.

"Well, I've been here for twenty years, and it's worn off. Sometimes I go back to visit for a while, and it comes back. I really like Atlantic City, but it's a little too close to home. My parents think I'm a dancer, and now that I'm a club owner, I don't have to pretend any more. It's a relief to stop hooking, I hated it. You've stopped too, haven't you Tina?"

"Yes, a few months ago. And then I met Steve. I'll never

go back to it again."

"Barbara," Steve said, "I just thought of something. What does Andrea do in regard to the actual workings of the club?"

"Andrea? I thought you knew. She doesn't do anything. Didn't want to. But, she put up $50,000 to make up for it. Her life savings; like she just wanted to get rid of it, to move onto something new."

Barbara then told us how she moved to L.A. in much the same manner as I did. She wanted to be a star. She hated prostitution, but kept going back to it. Finally, her madam moved to Las Vegas, for health reasons, and Barbara moved with her. Barbara was forty, the oldest in the group, but looked much younger.

I told her about my computer, Steve's craps ideas, and my studying to become a real accountant. She surprised us by saying she was also going to night school, to get her AA degree in management.

"I guess this club has changed you all. Is everything ready for the opening next month?" Steve asked.

"Yes. All of the girls have important friends and they've helped tremendously, so everything went smoothly. I'm sure we could open by Christmas but Yvonne wants to stick to New Years Eve, as per the advertising. So far, everything actually is going much better than we expected. Hamlish Construction has finished, the plumbing and lights work. Everything is ready, except the kitchen, and I don't expect any problems there."

"So," Steve asked, "the person I haven't met, Yvonne, is the Chief Executive Officer of this?"

"Yes. She got her degree in Business Administration, by going to school during the day while she was hooking at night. She became one of the highest paid working girls in Nevada, but I guess she got tired of it and wanted to try something new. Yvonne is really terrific, Steve. You'll have to meet her one day! You *are* coming to the opening?"

"Wouldn't miss it for the world." We chatted for a while, and Barbara said she had to go, so we all walked out of the mall, through the casino. We said goodbye to Barbara.

"Hey," said Steve, "I have an idea. Do you have keys to Oui Gals?

"Sure, why?"

"Can I see it now? Before the fuss and hoopla?"

"Sure," I said, suspecting something. And I thought I knew what it was.

We walked back to the car and drove to Boulder Highway. Oui Gals was standing there all alone, with an unlit sign that said "OPENING NEW YEARS EVE". We walked around to the back, and I used my keys to open the door. I turned on the lights and looked around. Everything still looked great, the booths, the tables, the decor.

Steve took my hand and we went to the booth furthest from the door. We both slid in. Now I was sure of what he wanted. We started kissing and soon my top was unbuttoned, as were Steve's pants. Before long, our clothes were all over the floor and table as we stretched out in one of the booths, kissing and caressing. I found him and put him inside of me. We both came very quickly. We hugged for a while, then left to go home.

I guess Oui Gals isn't a virgin anymore.

December

December is Rodeo Month in Las Vegas. The National Rodeo Finals and many lessor celebrations and shows are held here in the first two weeks.

We had the first taxi billboards up, advertising the Grand Opening of Oui Gals for New Years Eve. Steve would not be back until Christmas so I had the first three weeks to myself. I was busy publicizing Oui Gals, giving radio and television interviews, and talking to vendors. The building was finished. The sign was up. Everything was ready!

Most of the Rodeo show was at the Thomas and Mack Center, off the strip by the Las Vegas Hilton.

One of Andrea's friends was a publicity director and he somehow got us a speaking engagement at the Hilton, and its sister hotel, the Flamingo Hilton, which is on the strip. The Las Vegas Hilton has the most convention space in Las Vegas, and since it is so far from everything, meaning at least a ten minute walk, it is completely self sufficient with stores, restaurants, and even a baby sitting service. They don't want you to leave, *ever*.

The first speaking engagement, at the Las Vegas Hilton, didn't go over too well. There were eight of us scantily clad Oui Gals and we each talked for a minute, danced for a minute, and that was it. Polite applause. I guess the men were there for some Rodeo thing or, more likely, they expected us to strip, which we said in advance we wouldn't do. We did make sure that everyone leaving got a free drink coupon, though.

After the show, I decided to try the craps tables. There were eight of them, but only three were open. No one was yelling or screaming. I picked the one with the youngest looking people and bought in for $600. I tried everything, pass, don't pass, counting threes, but nothing worked. When I bet on the inside, I sevened out. When I bet don't come, numbers rolled. At the end of half an hour I was down $190, so I quit.

Let me say something here about money management. If I lose one third of my buy-in I will stop playing. I realize that even the best craps players lose sometimes. After all, it is a game of chance. Sometimes Mr. Dice just does not work for me, and I leave him alone. I don't believe in pouring good money after bad, so I always limit my losses to $200, assuming I buy in at $600.

The next day, at the Flamingo Hilton, our show was much better received. The talk and dance routine got a standing ovation, and some people actually asked for more free drink coupons! And, best of all, I won at the craps tables.

I was tired from the show, and didn't want to count anything. If a seven rolled, I would bet inside and take everything down after two hits. If a point was made, my next three bets were on the don't come. After a while I got tired and just watched. After a few rolls, I noticed that whenever a seven rolled, the stick man changed the positions of the dice so the seven wasn't showing, and then gave them to the new shooter. I asked the stick man what he was doing and he said that most people just don't want to see the seven face up.

I wondered about that for a while. Maybe if someone rolled the dice with the seven up they would do better, who knows. I didn't think the house would do something to help the players.

The Flamingo Hilton, where I was playing, is much smaller

than the Las Vegas Hilton, but it's gaudier and more personable at the same time. There are giant lighted Flamingo Plumes outside, and lots of noise and cheering inside. The Flamingo was the first real casino in Las Vegas, started by "Bugsy" Segal back in the 1940's. Now it seems to be the center of everything, surrounded by Ballys, Barbary Coast, and Harrahs. It is also right across the street from Caesars and the Mirage.

The Flamingo Hilton and the Stardust are the only two strip casinos I know of, that give you comp credit for your spread, instead of your individual bet. For example, at the Mirage, if you bet $20 pass line, and $24 six and eight, you are a $20 player. At the Flamingo Hilton and the Stardust you would be a $60 player. You get lots more comps this way.

Christmas finally arrived and I met Steve at the airport. After we kissed, the first words out of his mouth were that he had come up with yet another new craps system.

As we walked to my car, he explained it.

"It's not exactly a ground-breaking system, but it does work. I tried it out on a new craps simulation program called Wincraps. To start I wait for a seven and then bet $10 on the field, even before the point is established. If I win, I leave the bet up. If I win twice, I take it down. If it loses, I increase by one unit, to $20. If I lose again, I increase to $30. Then when I win, I backtrack. For example, if a field number didn't hit until I was at $50, I would take the $50 down, and wait for the next seven. Then I would start betting $50, then $40. Again, I'm looking for just two wins. If I won two, the next betting session would start where I left off. I would also stop betting on the field after five rolls, to minimize sevens."

"But," I said, "isn't the field a bad bet? Can't you make the 5, 6, 7 and 8 more times than the field numbers?"

"Well," Steve said, "you can make the 5, 6, 7 and 8 a total

of 20 times compared to 16 times for the field, but, without the seven, the field has a distinct advantage. Also, the 2 and 12 on the field pays double, which is a real bonus. And, by increasing my bets each time, I'm always making a profit, no matter what happens. That's the important part!"

I love it when he talks business.

"By the way," he said, "will Oui Gals open in time?"

"Oh yes! It's ready now, actually, but we're waiting for the official New Years Eve opening! And, it's sold out! It's going to be a big hit, the talk of the town!"

We were in my car, heading home.

"That's great, Tina! Looks like you have a real winner on your hands!"

Arriving at my condo, I took Steve's bag and put it outside my bedroom closet. I had set aside some space for him and couldn't help but wonder if we would live together permanently someday.

We finished unpacking and, without saying a word to each other, started undressing, and soon were naked and ravishing each other's bodies.

Later, Steve helped me with some computer problems. Computers sure are fun when they work the way you want them to. For the next week, we made love, and played craps a lot. At the casinos, we used Steve's new field bet system, and some old systems as well. The field system didn't work as well as we thought and we abandoned it. Too much work for too little money. Fortunately, there are many good craps systems out there and Steve and I wanted to try them all! It's a learning experience, after all.

One day we took a helicopter tour of the Grand Canyon and it was wonderful. We fell in love all over again.

When December 31st finally arrived, Steve rented a tux, and I rented a beautiful sequined light green designer gown that sparkled when I moved. When we arrived at Oui Gals, it was already crowded. Yvonne, Andrea and Barbara all brought dates, and I was there with my wonderful lover and craps partner, Steve.

Steve finally met Yvonne, and was suitably impressed. She did look gorgeous! I got the surprise of my life when I met the President of Hamlish Construction. He was a tall, red headed, well built, clean shaven, handsome man - Marvin Hamlish - formerly known as Big Red!

"You look terrific! What happened?" I gasped.

"Well," Marv said, "you had a lot to do with it. I thought about what you said for a long time, and you were right. If I could be successful at craps, I could be successful at anything, including improving myself. I went on a strict diet and started going to the gym every day. It was very hard, harder than anything I've ever done, but I did it. When I read about your club in the paper, I wanted to be the contractor. I did everything I could, at the best price. It's funny, but now that I'm in good shape, people are judging me by what I've done and want to accomplish, rather than by my looks. And it's all due to you, and your wonderful honesty and insights. Tina, I want to thank you from the bottom of my heart!"

We hugged and Yvonne came up and started talking to him. I turned around, and there was someone else from my past, Jack, the dealer from Binions.

"Hi," he said. "Tina, I'd like you to meet my wife, Joan."

"Hello, Tina," she said. "Jack has told me *everything* about you, and then some. I'm glad we finally met. Jack has stopped gambling now, thanks to you. I'm really glad he met you, however strange the circumstances. It's so refreshing to have a real, honest, dependable husband again."

Wow, I guess honesty really is the best policy, after all!

We talked for a while and then Barbara, Andrea, and

Yvonne came by, with champagne glasses in their hands for all of us.

"To Oui Gals," Yvonne said, and we all drank a toast. Reporters took our pictures and asked us questions. More and more people poured in.

Midnight arrived and Steve held me close. "I love you, Tina," he said.

"I love you too, Steve." We kissed, long and hard.

Steve had a gleam in his eyes. "Now that you're a craps expert, and your club is off to a rousing start, what are you going to do next?"

"I don't know," I said. "Say, what do you know about Blackjack?" We both laughed, but I already was getting ideas. I could buy a mini-blackjack table . . .

Tina Trapp's Glossary of Craps Terminology

Any Craps - Single bet for the numbers 2, 3, or 12

Big Dick - Slang expression for the number 10

Big Red - Slang expression for the number 7

Boxcars - Slang expression for the number twelve

Boxman - A seated casino employee who supervises the craps game

Buy bets - Paying commission to get true odds

Buy-In - When you start playing and buy chips

C and E bet - Any craps plus eleven, one time bet

Call bet - A verbal wager by experienced, known players

Cold Dice - Dice that rarely make the point

Color Out - To exchange chips for money

Come Bet - Your own personal point bet

Come-out roll - The first roll of a new shooter

Comps - Free room, food and beverage for qualified gamblers

Craps - When the dice total 2, 3, or 12

Crossroader - Slang expression for a crook or cheater

Dimes - Slang term for $10 in chips

Don't Come Bet - A separate bet against a point passing

Down - To take money off a bet

Easy - A number not made with two identical pairs

Eighter from Decatur - slang term for the number eight

Field Bet - The numbers 2, 3, 4, 9, 10, 11, 12

Free Odds - Odds portion of bet that has no house advantage

Fun Book - Free coupon book available at most cashier cages

George - Slang term for a player that is a good tipper

Grinder - Someone who always takes bets down after they win

Hardway - A number made with two identical pairs

High Roller - A gambler that bets more than $100 per hand

Hop Bet - An oral one roll bet for a specific number

Horn Bet - A one roll bet on the 2, 3, 11 and 12

Hot Dice - Dice that usually make the point

Inside bet - The numbers 5, 6, 8 and 9

Jimmy Sticks - Slang term for the number 6

Junket - RFB plus travel for experienced gamblers

Lay bet - A bet that the seven will roll before a specific number

Little Joe from Kokomo - Slang term for the number four

Limits - Posted table maximum and minimum bets

Lumpy - Slang term for a brand new dealer

Marker - An IOU check signed by a player

Natural - Rolling seven or eleven on the come-out

Nickels - Slang term for $5 chips

Off - An oral request to have bets not working

Off and On - Being paid for a bet while leaving the same bet up

Outside bet - The numbers 4, 5, 9 and 10

Parlay - When the entire win is added to the bet

Pass - A winner for the shooter

Pit Boss - High level casino employee in charge of games

Place Bet - Any of the numbers 4, 5, 6, 8, 9 or 10

Point - The number 4, 5, 6, 8, 9, or 10 when rolled on the come-out

Press - To increase the bet

Proposition Bets - Center spread table bets

Push - A tie between the casino and bettor

Quarters - Slang term for $25 chips

RFB - Complimentary room food and beverage

Right Bettor - Bettor betting that shooter makes his point

Shill - A person secretly employed by the casino

Snake Eyes - Slang term for the number two

Stickman - The dealer in charge of the dice

Toke - A tip for the dealer

Two-way bet - One bet for yourself, and one for the dealer

Unit - A fixed amount of bet, usually the initial bet

Vig - A commission paid to the house for certain bets

Working - To have bets "On" during the come-out

World Bet - Any horn number or seven, one roll bet

Wrong Bettor - Bettor betting that shooter does not make his point

Yo - Slang term for eleven

Tina Trapp's Resource Guide

Casino Journal 1-800-969-0711
Mostly for Casino personnel and industry insiders - Free
sample copy on request

Casino Player 1-800-969-0711
A good, general purpose gambling magazine, emphasis on
Las Vegas and Atlantic City - Free sample copy on request

Las Vegas Advisor 1-800-244-2224
Terrific newsletter for visitors to Las Vegas - Sample $5.00

The Crapshooter, Box 421440, San Diego, CA 92142
The only newsletter devoted exclusively to the game of
craps. Special subscriber discounts - Sample copy $5.00

Gambler's Book Club 1-800-522-1777
Gambling book store sells books, magazines, videos and
software, does mail order - Free catalog on request

Gambler's General Store 1-800-322-CHIP
Gambling store sells equipment, books and chips, does mail
order - Catalog $3.00 refundable with order

Gambler's Bookstore 1-800-816-6681
Gambling store sells equipment, books and chips, does mail
order - Free catalog on request